PEARSON CUSTOM LIBRARY

Introductory Chemistry
Chemistry 101

PEARSON

Cover Art: Courtesy of Photodisc, Photodisc/Getty Images, Age Fotostock America, Inc., and Photo Researchers, and Getty Images. "Atom. Elementary Particle. 3D Background of Nuclear Physics." courtesy of Aleksandr Bedrin/Fotolia. "3D rendered silver glossy core molecules structure High resolution" courtesy of Iaroslav Neliubov/Shutterstock.

Attention bookstores: For permission to return unused stock, contact us at *pe-uscustomreturns@pearson.com*.

Pearson Learning Solutions, 501 Boylston Street, Suite 900, Boston, MA 02116
A Pearson Education Company
www.pearsoned.com

Printed in the United States of America.

ISBN 10: 1-269-68303-9
ISBN 13: 978-1-269-68303-6

34 2019

Table of Contents

Periodic Table of the Elements

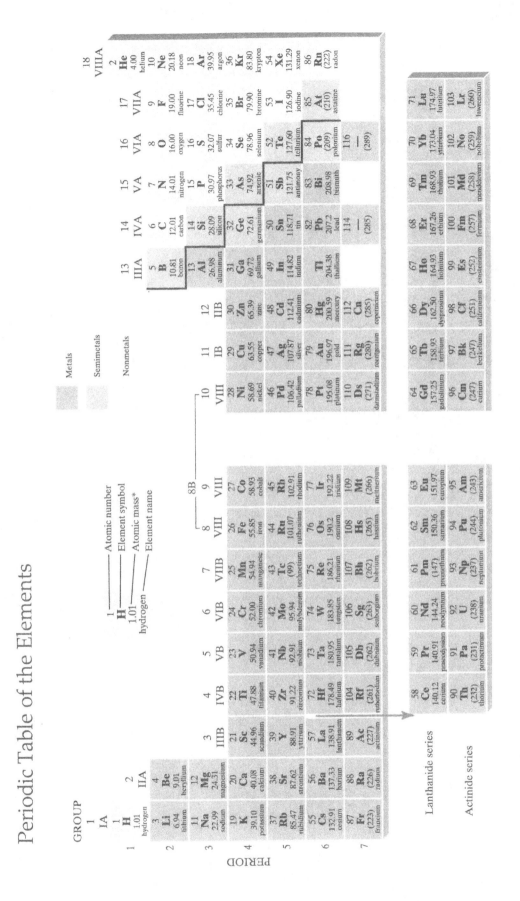

Safety Precautions

With proper precautions, a chemistry laboratory should not be a dangerous place. If you do the prelaboratory assignment and check your answers at the end of the experiment before coming to lab, the laboratory should be safe to do your experiments. The following rules are common sense.

1. Wear approved safety goggles while working in the laboratory.
2. Wear shoes (not sandals) while working in the laboratory.
3. Do not bring food or drink into the laboratory.
4. Locate the fire extinguisher(s).
5. Locate the first-aid equipment.
6. Do not perform unauthorized experiments.
7. Do not smell a gas directly; instead gently waft the vapor toward your nose.

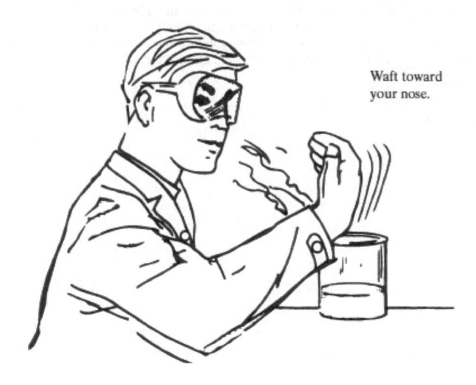

Waft toward your nose.

8. Perform experiments that produce a gas under a fume hood.
9. When heating a test tube, point the open end in a safe direction.

10. Always pour an acid into water—not water into acid.
11. Clean up broken glass immediately.
12. Do not use an organic liquid near an open flame in the laboratory.
    Organic liquids, such as acetone and alcohol, are highly flammable.
13. If you contact a chemical, wash immediately with water and notify the Instructor.
14. Notify the Instructor immediately in the event of an accident.

Instrumental Measurements

OBJECTIVES

- To obtain measurements of length, mass, volume, and temperature.
- To determine the mass and volume of an unknown rectangular solid.
- To gain proficiency in using the following instruments: metric rulers, balances, graduated cylinder, and thermometer.

DISCUSSION

The **metric system** uses a basic set of units and prefixes. The basic unit of length is the meter, the basic unit of mass is the gram, and the basic unit of volume is the liter. Metric prefixes make these basic units larger or smaller by powers of 10. For example, a kilometer is a thousand times longer than a meter, and a meter is a thousand times longer than a millimeter. In the laboratory, the most common unit of length is **centimeter** (symbol **cm**), the most common unit of mass is **gram** (symbol **g**), and the most common unit of volume is **milliliter** (symbol **mL**).

Scientific instruments have evolved to a high state of sensitivity. However, it is not possible to make an exact measurement. The reason is that all instruments possess a degree of **uncertainty**—no matter how sensitive. The uncertainty is indicated by the significant digits in the measurement. For example, a metric ruler may measure length to the nearest tenth of a centimeter (± 0.1 cm). A different metric ruler may measure length to the nearest five hundredths of a centimeter (± 0.05 cm). The measurement with the least uncertainty (± 0.05 cm) is more precise.

From Experiment 2 of *Laboratory Manual to Accompany Introductory Chemistry: Concepts and Critical Thinking*, Sixth Edition. Charles H. Corwin.

In this experiment, we will use several instruments. We will make measurements of mass with balances having progressively greater sensitivity. A decigram balance is so named because the uncertainty is one-tenth of a gram (± 0.1 g). The uncertainty of a centigram balance is one-hundredth of a gram (± 0.01 g), and the uncertainty of a milligram balance is one-thousandth of a gram (± 0.001 g).

We will make length measurements using two metric rulers that differ in their uncertainty. METRIC RULER A is calibrated in 1-cm divisions and has an uncertainty of ± 0.1 cm. METRIC RULER B has 0.1-cm subdivisions and an uncertainty of ± 0.05 cm. Thus, METRIC RULER B has less uncertainty than METRIC RULER A. The following examples demonstrate measurement of length utilizing the two different metric rulers.

Example Exercise 1 • Measuring Length with Metric Ruler A

A copper rod is measured with the metric ruler shown below. What is the length of the rod?

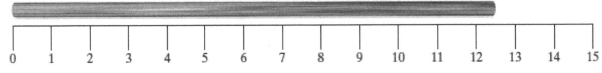

METRIC RULER A   *(Estimate to a tenth of a division ±0.1 cm)*

Solution: Each division represents one centimeter. The end of the rod lies between the 12th and 13th divisions. We can estimate to a tenth of a division (± 0.1 cm). Since the end of the rod lies about five-tenths past 12, we can estimate the length as

$$12 \text{ cm} + 0.5 \text{ cm} = 12.5 \text{ cm}$$

Example Exercise 2 • Measuring Length with Metric Ruler B

The same copper rod is measured with the metric ruler shown below. What is the length of the rod?

METRIC RULER B   *(Estimate to a half of a subdivision ±0.05 cm)*

Solution: Note that this ruler is divided into centimeters that are subdivided into tenths of centimeters. The end of the rod lies between the 12th and 13th divisions and between the 5th and 6th subdivisions. Thus, the length is between 12.5 cm and 12.6 cm.

We can estimate the measurement more precisely. A subdivision is too small to divide into ten parts, but we can estimate to half of a subdivision (± 0.05 cm). The length is 12 cm + 0.5 cm + 0.05 cm = 12.55 cm.

To test your skill in making metric measurements, you will determine the mass and volume of an unknown rectangular solid. The volume of a rectangular solid is calculated from its length, width, and thickness. The following examples will illustrate.

Example Exercise 3 • Calculating Volume of a Rectangular Solid

An unknown rectangular solid was measured with METRIC RULER A, which provided the following: 5.0 cm by 2.5 cm by 1.1 cm. What is the volume of the solid?

Solution: The volume of a rectangular solid equals length times width times thickness.

$$5.0 \text{ cm} \times 2.5 \text{ cm} \times 1.1 \text{ cm} = 13.75 \text{ cm}^3 = 14 \text{ cm}^3$$

In this example, each measurement has two significant digits; thus, the volume has two significant digits. Note the unit of volume is cubic centimeter, cm^3.

Example Exercise 4 • Calculating Volume of a Rectangular Solid

The unknown rectangular solid was also measured with METRIC RULER B, which gave the following: 5.00 cm by 2.45 cm by 1.15 cm. What is the volume of the solid?

Solution: The volume of a rectangular solid equals length times width times thickness.

$$5.00 \text{ cm} \times 2.45 \text{ cm} \times 1.15 \text{ cm} = 14.0875 \text{ cm}^3 = 14.1 \text{ cm}^3$$

In this example, each measurement has three significant digits; thus, the volume has three significant digits.

We can measure the volume of a liquid using a graduated cylinder. If we carefully examine the 100-mL graduated cylinder shown in Figure 1, we notice that it is marked in 10-mL intervals, and each interval has ten subdivisions. Therefore, each subdivision equals one milliliter. If we estimate to half of a subdivision, the uncertainty is ± 0.5 mL.

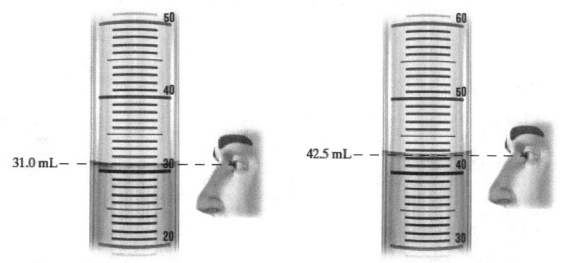

Figure 1 Graduated Cylinder Example readings using proper eye position and recording the bottom of the **meniscus** to half a subdivision (± 0.5 mL).

We can measure temperature using a Celsius thermometer. If we examine the thermometer shown in Figure 2, we notice that it is marked in 10 °C intervals that have ten subdivisions. Thus, each subdivision equals one degree Celsius. If we estimate to half of a subdivision, the temperature measurement has an uncertainty of ± 0.5 °C.

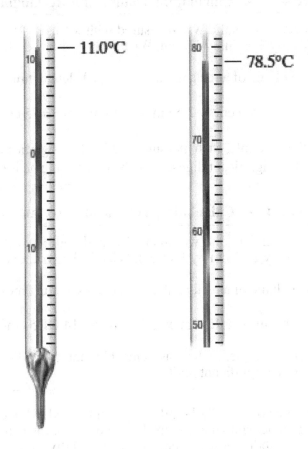

Figure 2 Celsius Thermometer Example readings using a Celsius thermometer and recording the top of the liquid to half a subdivision (± 0.5 °C).

EQUIPMENT and CHEMICALS

- 13 x 100 mm test tubes (3)
- watchglass
- evaporating dish
- crucible & cover
- 125-mL Erlenmeyer flask
- 100-mL graduated cylinder
- dropper pipet
- 250-mL beaker with ice
- 150-mL beaker
- 110 °C thermometer
- ring stand & ring

- ring stand & ring
- wire gauze
- decigram balance
- centigram balance
- milligram balance
- unknown rectangular solid

PROCEDURE

A. Length Measurements

1. Measure the length of a 13 x 100 mm test tube with each of the following: (a) METRIC RULER A, and (b) METRIC RULER B.

   Note: Refer to METRIC RULER A instructions in **Example Exercise 1**.
   Refer to METRIC RULER B instructions in **Example Exercise 2**.

2. Measure the diameter of a watchglass with each of the following: (a) METRIC RULER A, and (b) METRIC RULER B.

3. Measure the diameter of an evaporating dish (not the spout) with each of the following: (a) METRIC RULER A, and (b) METRIC RULER B.

B. Mass Measurements

1. Determine the mass of an evaporating dish on the following balances: (a) decigram balance, (b) centigram balance, and (c) milligram balance.

2. Determine the mass of a crucible and cover on the following balances: (a) decigram balance, (b) centigram balance, and (c) milligram balance.

3. Determine the mass of a 125-mL Erlenmeyer flask on the following balances: (a) decigram balance, (b) centigram balance, and (c) milligram balance.

C. Mass and Volume of an Unknown Solid

1. Obtain a rectangular solid and record the unknown number in the Data Table. Find the mass of the unknown rectangular solid using each of the following: (a) a decigram balance, (b) a centigram balance, and (c) a milligram balance.

2. Measure the length, width, and thickness of the rectangular solid unknown using METRIC RULER A shown in Example Exercise 1. Calculate the volume.

3. Measure the length, width, and thickness of the rectangular solid unknown using METRIC RULER B shown in Example Exercise 2. Calculate the volume.

D. Volume Measurements

1. Fill a 100-mL graduated cylinder with water. Adjust the bottom of the meniscus to the full mark with a dropper pipet. Record the volume as 100.0 mL.

2. Fill a 13 x 100 mm test tube with water from the graduated cylinder. Record the new volume in the graduated cylinder ($\pm$ 0.5 mL).

   Note: Refer to the graduated cylinder instructions in **Figure 1**.

3. Fill a second test tube with water. Record the volume in the graduated cylinder.

E. Temperature Measurements

1. Record the temperature in the laboratory using a Celsius thermometer (± 0.5 °C).

2. Half-fill a 250-mL beaker with ice and water. Hold the thermometer in the ice water and record the coldest observed temperature (± 0.5 °C).

3. Half-fill a 150-mL beaker with distilled water. Support the beaker on a ring stand with a wire gauze as shown in Figure 3. Heat the water to boiling and shut off the burner. Place the thermometer in the boiling water and record the temperature (± 0.5 °C).

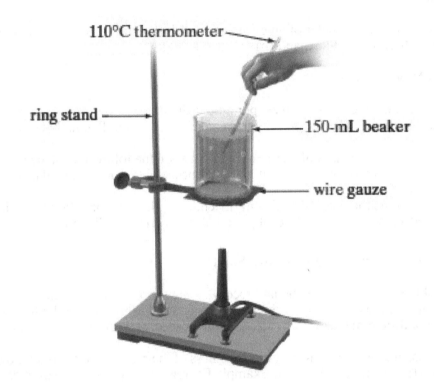

Figure 3 Apparatus for Boiling Water To obtain an accurate temperature measurement, do not allow the thermometer to touch the hot glass beaker.

EXPERIMENT _____   NAME _____

DATE _____   SECTION _____

PRELABORATORY ASSIGNMENT*

1. Provide the key term that corresponds to each of the following definitions.

    _____ (a) a decimal system of measurement using prefixes and a basic unit to express length, mass, and volume

    _____ (b) a metric unit of length

    _____ (c) a metric unit of mass

    _____ (d) a metric unit of volume

    _____ (e) the clear lens at the surface of a liquid inside a graduated cylinder

    _____ (f) the degree of inexactness in an instrumental measurement

    Key Terms: centimeter (cm), gram (g), meniscus, metric system, milliliter (mL), uncertainty

2. State the length measurement indicated on each of the following metric rulers.

    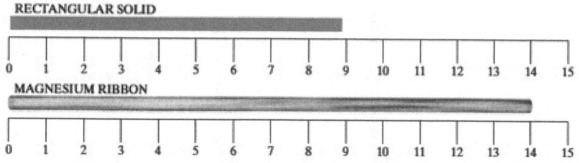

3. A rectangular solid measures 5.0 cm by 2.5 cm by 1.5 cm. Refer to Example Exercise 3 and show the calculation for volume of the rectangular solid.

4. State the length measurement indicated on each of the following metric rulers.

    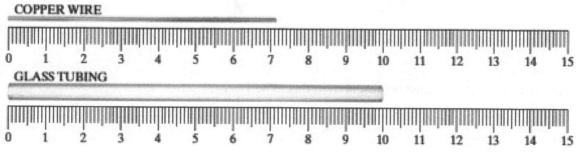

---

* Answers at the end of the experiment.

5. A rectangular solid measures 5.05 cm by 2.45 cm by 1.50 cm. Refer to Example Exercise 4 and show the calculation for volume of the rectangular solid.

6. State the volume measurement indicated by each of the following graduated cylinders.

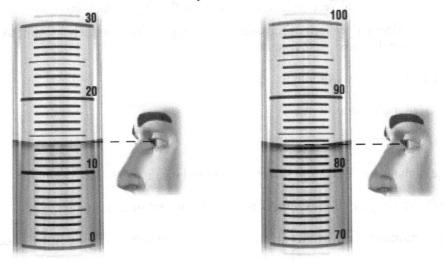

7. State the temperature measurement indicated by each of the following Celsius thermometers.

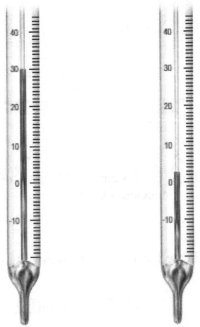

8. What safety precautions must be observed in this experiment?

EXPERIMENT   NAME _____

DATE _____   SECTION _____

DATA TABLE

A. Length Measurements

length of a 13 x 100 mm test tube

     METRIC RULER A   _____ cm

     METRIC RULER B   _____ cm

diameter of a watchglass

     METRIC RULER A   _____ cm

     METRIC RULER B   _____ cm

diameter of an evaporating dish

     METRIC RULER A   _____ cm

     METRIC RULER B   _____ cm

B. Mass Measurements

mass of an evaporating dish

     decigram balance   _____ g

     centigram balance   _____ g

     milligram balance   _____ g

mass of a crucible and cover

     decigram balance   _____ g

     centigram balance   _____ g

     milligram balance   _____ g

mass of a 125-mL Erlenmeyer flask

     decigram balance   _____ g

     centigram balance   _____ g

     milligram balance   _____ g

C. Mass and Volume of an Unknown Solid   **UNKNOWN #** _____

    mass of unknown solid

        decigram balance   _____ g

        centigram balance   _____ g

        milligram balance   _____ g

    volume of unknown solid (METRIC RULER A)

        length of solid   _____ cm

        width of solid   _____ cm

        thickness of solid   _____ cm

Show the calculation for the volume of the rectangular solid (see Example Exercise 3).

               _____ cm^3

    volume of unknown solid (METRIC RULER B)

        length of solid   _____ cm

        width of solid   _____ cm

        thickness of solid   _____ cm

Show the calculation for the volume of the rectangular solid (see Example Exercise 4).

               _____ cm^3

D. Volume Measurements

    volume of water in a graduated cylinder   _____ mL

    volume minus one test tube of water   _____ mL

    volume minus two test tubes of water   _____ mL

E. Temperature Measurements

    room temperature   _____ °C

    melting point temperature of ice   _____ °C

    boiling point temperature of water   _____ °C

EXPERIMENT   NAME _____

DATE _____   SECTION _____

POSTLABORATORY ASSIGNMENT

1. State the basic unit in the metric system for each of the following.

    (a) length   _____   (b) mass   _____

    (c) volume   _____   (d) temperature   _____

2. State a common laboratory instrument for measuring each of the following.

    (a) diameter of a beaker _____   (b) mass of a sample   _____

    (c) volume of water   _____   (d) temperature of air _____

3. State the metric unit associated with each of the following instruments.

    (a) metric ruler   _____   (b) balance   _____

    (c) graduated cylinder _____   (d) thermometer   _____

4. Select the measurement that is consistent with the uncertainty of each instrument.

    (a) METRIC RULER A: 5 cm, 5.0 cm, 5.00 cm   _____

    (b) METRIC RULER B: 5 cm, 5.0 cm, 5.00 cm   _____

    (c) decigram balance: 5.0 g, 5.00 g, 5.000 g   _____

    (d) centigram balance: 5.0 g, 5.00 g, 5.000 g   _____

    (e) milligram balance: 5.0 g, 5.00 g, 5.000 g   _____

    (f) graduated cylinder: 5 mL, 5.0 mL, 5.00 mL   _____

    (g) Celsius thermometer: 5 °C, 5.0 °C, 5.00 °C   _____

5. State the uncertainty (for example, ± 0.5 cm) in each of the following measurements.

    (a) 25.00 cm   _____   (b) 25.000 g   _____

    (c) 25.0 mL   _____   (d) 25.0 °C   _____

15

6. State the number of significant digits in each of the following measurements.

    (a) 5.00 cm   _____   (b)   0.50 cm   _____

    (c) 0.500 g   _____   (d)   0.005 g   _____

    (e) 50.0 mL   _____   (f)   5.5 mL   _____

    (g) 50.5 °C   _____   (h)   –0.5 °C   _____

7. Perform the indicated math operation and round off the answer to the proper significant digits.

    (a)   50.511 g   (b)   97.5   g
          +   10.25 g   –   95.826 g

8. Perform the indicated math operation and round off the answer to the proper significant digits.

    (a)   (5.15 cm) (2.25 cm) (1.0 cm)   (b) $\dfrac{15.15 \text{ cm}^3}{12.0 \text{ cm}^2}$

9. Explain why you round off the numbers in a calculator display after addition, subtraction, multiplication, or division of measurements.

10. (optional) A platinum cylinder has a mass of 1.000 kg, a diameter of 3.90 cm, and a height of 3.90 cm. What is the volume of the cylinder in grams per cubic centimeter? The volume of a cylinder equals $\pi d^2 h/4$, where π is 3.14, d is the diameter, and h is the height.

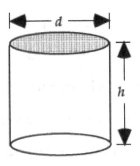

Density of Liquids and Solids

OBJECTIVES

- To observe the relative density of common liquids and solids.
- To determine the density of water, an unknown liquid, a rubber stopper, and an unknown rectangular solid.
- To determine the thickness of a piece of aluminum foil using the density concept.
- To gain proficiency in performing the following experimental procedures: pipetting a liquid, weighing by difference, and determining a volume by displacement.

DISCUSSION

Density is a physical property of liquids and solids. We can define **density** (symbol d) as the amount of mass in a given volume. To determine the density of a solid experimentally, we must measure the mass of the solid using a balance. To determine the mass of a liquid, we use an indirect technique called **weighing by difference** (Figure 1). First, we weigh a flask empty. Second, we add a given volume of liquid into the flask and reweigh. The mass of the liquid is found by subtracting the first mass reading from the second mass reading.

After collecting the experimental data, we can calculate density by dividing the mass by the volume. It is important, however, that we attach the proper units to the calculated value. The density of liquids and solids is usually expressed in grams per milliliter (g/mL) or grams per cubic centimeter (g/cm^3). Since 1 mL = 1 cm^3, the numerical value for density in g/mL and g/cm^3 is identical. For example, the density of water may be expressed as 1.00 g/mL or 1.00 g/cm^3.

From Experiment 3 of *Laboratory Manual to Accompany Introductory Chemistry: Concepts and Critical Thinking*, Sixth Edition. Charles H. Corwin. Copyright © 2013 by Pearson Education, Inc. All rights reserved.

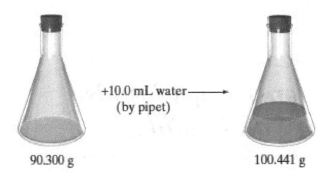

90.300 g   100.441 g

Figure 1 Weighing by Difference The mass of the liquid is found by the
difference in masses: 100.441 g – 90.300 g = 10.141 g.

Example Exercise 1 • Density of a Liquid

A 10.0-mL sample of water is pipetted into a flask. The mass of water, 10.141 g, is found
after weighing by difference (see Figure 1). Calculate the density of water.

Solution: Dividing the mass of water by volume, we have

$$\frac{10.141 \text{ g}}{10.0 \text{ mL}} = 1.01 \text{ g/mL}$$

We round the answer to three significant digits because there are only three
digits in the denominator. In this example, the calculated value, 1.01 g/mL,
agrees closely with the theoretical value, 1.00 g/mL. The slight discrepancy is
due to experimental error.

The volume of an irregular object can be found indirectly from the amount of water it
displaces. This technique is called **volume by displacement**. For example, the volume of a rubber
stopper can be determined as shown in Figure 2. The initial reading of water in the graduated
cylinder is observed. The stopper is introduced into the graduated cylinder and the final reading is
recorded. The difference between the initial and final readings corresponds to the volume of water
displaced. The volume of water displaced is equal to the volume of the rubber stopper.

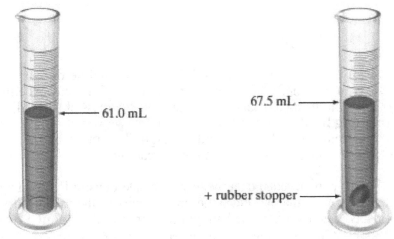

Figure 2 Volume by Displacement The volume of the rubber stopper is found
by the increase in volume: 67.5 mL – 61.0 mL = 6.5 mL.

Example Exercise 2 • Density of a Rubber Stopper

A rubber stopper weighing 8.453 g displaces 6.5 mL of water in a graduated cylinder (Figure 2). What is the density of the rubber stopper?

Solution: Dividing the mass of the rubber stopper by its volume, we have

$$\frac{8.453 \text{ g}}{6.5 \text{ mL}} = 1.3 \text{ g/mL}$$

In this example, the volume has two significant digits. Thus, the density of the rubber stopper is limited to two digits.

We will also determine the density of a solid. The volume of any solid object with regular dimensions can be found by calculation. For example, the volume of a rectangular solid object is calculated by multiplying its length times its width times its thickness.

Example Exercise 3 • Density of a Rectangular Solid

The mass of an unknown rectangular block is 139.443 g. If the block measures 5.00 cm by 2.55 cm by 1.25 cm, what is its density?

Solution: First, we calculate the volume of the rectangular block.

$$5.00 \text{ cm} \times 2.55 \text{ cm} \times 1.25 \text{ cm} = 15.9 \text{ cm}^3$$

Second, we find the density of the unknown rectangular solid.

$$\frac{139.443 \text{ g}}{15.9 \text{ cm}^3} = 8.77 \text{ g/cm}^3$$

The thickness of aluminum foil is too thin to measure with a ruler. However, we can find the thickness of the foil indirectly. Given the mass and density of the foil, we can calculate the volume. From the volume, length, and width of the foil, we can calculate the thickness.

Example Exercise 4 • Thickness of an Aluminum Foil

A piece of aluminum foil has a mass of 0.450 g and measures 10.75 cm by 10.10 cm. Given the density of aluminum, 2.70 g/cm^3, calculate the thickness of the foil.

Solution: To calculate the thickness of the foil, we must first find the volume. The volume can be calculated using density as a unit factor.

$$0.450 \text{ g} \times \frac{1 \text{ cm}^3}{2.70 \text{ g}} = 0.167 \text{ cm}^3$$

The thickness is found after dividing the volume by its length and width.

$$\frac{0.167 \text{ cm}^3}{(10.75 \text{ cm})(10.10 \text{ cm})} = 0.00154 \text{ cm} \quad (1.54 \times 10^{-3} \text{ cm})$$

EQUIPMENT and CHEMICALS

A. Instructor Demonstration

- tall glass cylinder
- corn syrup
- mineral oil

- glass marble
- rubber stopper
- ice
- cork

B–F. Student Experiments
- 125-mL Erlenmeyer flask
  with rubber stopper to fit
- 150-mL beaker
- 100-mL beaker
- 10-mL pipet & bulb

- 100-mL graduated cylinder
- #2 rubber stopper
- unknown liquids
- unknown rectangular solids
- aluminum foil, ~ 10 x 10 cm rectangle

PROCEDURE

A. Instructor Demonstration – Density

RECYCLE
Chemical
Waste

1. Add ~100 mL of corn syrup into a tall glass cylinder.

2. Slowly add ~200 mL of water into the cylinder.

3. Slowly add ~100 mL of mineral oil into the cylinder.

4. Slowly slide a glass marble into the tall glass cylinder.

5. Slowly slide a rubber stopper into the cylinder.

6. Slowly slide a piece of ice into the cylinder.

7. Drop a cork into the cylinder.

B. Density of Water

The Instructor may demonstrate how to *condition* a pipet and *transfer* a sample liquid.

1. Weigh a 125-mL Erlenmeyer flask fitted with a rubber stopper.

2. Half-fill a 150-mL beaker with distilled water, and then pipet a 10.0-mL sample into the 125-mL flask.

3. Reweigh the flask and stopper, and determine the mass of water by difference.

4. Repeat a second trial for the density of the water.

> **Note**: It is not necessary to dry the flask between trials because the 10.0-mL sample of water is weighed by difference.

5. Calculate the density of water for each trial, and report the average value for both trials.

C. Density of an Unknown Liquid

1. Obtain about 25 mL of an unknown liquid in a 100-mL beaker. Record the unknown number in the Data Table.

2. Weigh a 125-mL Erlenmeyer flask fitted with a rubber stopper.

3. Condition a pipet with unknown liquid, and transfer a 10.0-mL sample into the flask.

4. Reweigh the flask and stopper, and determine the mass of liquid by difference.

5. Repeat a second trial for the density of the unknown liquid.

6. Calculate the density of the unknown liquid and report the average value for both trials.

D. Density of a Rubber Stopper

1. Weigh a dry #2 rubber stopper.

2. Half-fill a 100-mL graduated cylinder with water. Observe the bottom of the meniscus and estimate the volume to ±0.5 mL (see Figure 3).

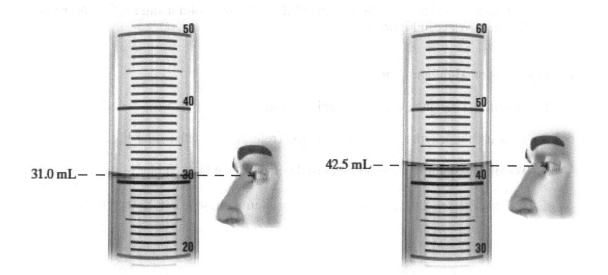

Figure 3 Graduated Cylinder Example readings using proper eye position and recording the bottom of the **meniscus** to half a subdivision (± 0.5 mL).

3. Tilt the graduated cylinder, and let the stopper slowly slide into the water. Observe the new water level, and calculate the volume by displacement for the stopper.

4. Repeat a second trial for the density of the rubber stopper.

5. Calculate the density of the rubber stopper and report the average value for both trials.

E. Density of an Unknown Solid

   1. Obtain a rectangular solid, and record the unknown number in the Data Table.

   2. Weigh the unknown solid and record the mass.

   3. Measure and record the length, width, and thickness of the unknown rectangular solid, using the metric ruler in Figure 3.

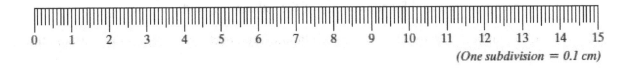

(One subdivision = 0.1 cm)

Figure 3 Metric Ruler The uncertainty of the measurement is ±0.05 cm.

   4. Calculate the volume of the unknown rectangular solid.

   5. Repeat a second trial for the volume of the unknown solid using a different balance and the metric ruler in Figure 3.

F. Thickness of Aluminum Foil

   1. Obtain a rectangular piece of aluminum foil.

   2. Measure the length and width of the foil (refer to the metric ruler Figure 3).

   3. Weigh the aluminum foil and record the mass in the Data Table.

   4. Calculate the volume and thickness of the aluminum foil ($d = 2.70$ g/cm^3).

EXPERIMENT   NAME   _____

DATE   _____   SECTION   _____

PRELABORATORY ASSIGNMENT*

1. Provide the key term that corresponds to each of the following definitions.

    _____ (a) the amount of mass in a unit volume of matter; for example, 1.00 g/mL

    _____ (b) a procedure for obtaining the mass of a sample by first weighing a container
    and then weighing the container with the sample

    _____ (c) the degree of inexactness in an instrumental measurement

    _____ (d) to rinse glassware (e.g., a pipet) with a sample liquid to avoid dilution
    by water on the inside surface

    _____ (e) the clear lens at the surface of a liquid inside a graduated cylinder

    _____ (f) determining volume of a sample by measuring the volume of water displaced

        Key Terms: condition, density, meniscus, uncertainty, volume by displacement, weighing
    by difference

2. A 10.0-mL sample of liquid is pipetted into a 125-mL flask with stopper. The mass of liquid is
    found to be 7.988 g. Refer to Example Exercise 1 and calculate the density of the liquid.

3. State the volume of liquid shown in each of the following graduated cylinders.

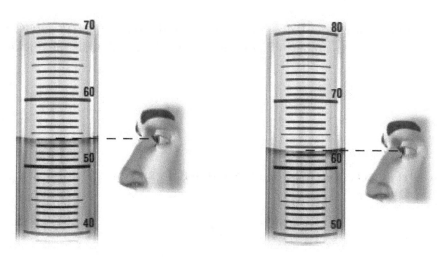

_____

Answers at the end of the experiment.

4. A rubber stopper has a mass of 7.452 g and displaces 6.0 mL of water in a graduated cylinder. Refer to Example Exercise 2 and calculate the density of the rubber stopper.

5. State the length shown for each of the following rectangular solids.

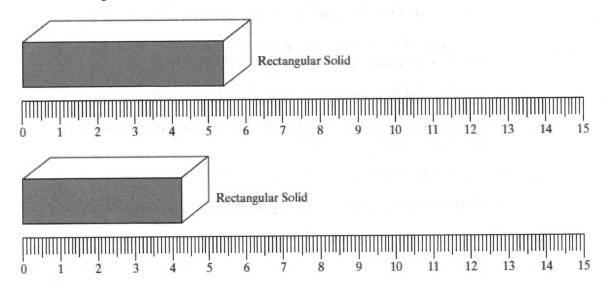

6. An unknown rectangular solid has a mass of 140.417 g and measures 5.05 cm by 2.50 cm by 1.25 cm. Refer to Example Exercise 3 and calculate the density of the unknown solid.

7. An aluminum foil weighs 0.465 g and measures 10.10 cm by 10.05 cm. Given the density of aluminum, 2.70 g/cm³, refer to Example Exercise 4 and calculate the thickness of the foil.

8. What safety precautions must be observed in this experiment?

EXPERIMENT   NAME   _____

DATE   _____   SECTION   _____

DATA TABLE

A. Instructor Demonstration – Density

- *corn syrup*

- *water*

- *mineral oil*

- *glass marble*

- *rubber stopper*

- *ice*

- *cork*

Identify the liquids (L_1, L_2) and solids (S_1, S_2, S_3, S_4) in the tall glass cylinder.

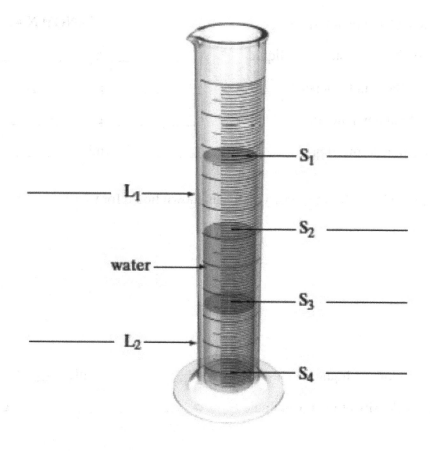

RECYCLE
Chemical
Waste

B. Density of Water

mass of flask and stopper + water   _____ g   _____ g

mass of flask and stopper   _____ g   _____ g

mass of water   _____ g   _____ g

volume of water   _____ mL   _____ mL

Show the calculation for the density of water for trial 1 (see Example Exercise 1).

Density of water   _____ g/mL   _____ g/mL

Average density of water   _____ g/mL

C. Density of an Unknown Liquid   **UNKNOWN #** _____

mass of flask and stopper + liquid   _____ g   _____ g

mass of flask and stopper   _____ g   _____ g

mass of unknown liquid   _____ g   _____ g

volume of unknown liquid   _____ mL   _____ mL

Show the calculation for the density of the unknown liquid for trial 1.

Density of unknown liquid   _____ g/mL   _____ g/mL

Average density of unknown liquid   _____ g/mL

RECYCLE
Chemical
Waste

D. Density of a Rubber Stopper

       mass of a rubber stopper   _____ g   _____ g

       final graduated cylinder reading   _____ mL   _____ mL

       initial graduated cylinder reading   _____ mL   _____ mL

       volume of rubber stopper   _____ mL   _____ mL

Show the calculation of density for the stopper for trial 1 (see Example Exercise 2).

       Density of rubber stopper   _____ g/mL _____ g/mL

         Average density of rubber stopper   _____ g/mL

E. Density of an Unknown Solid   **UNKNOWN #** _____

       mass of solid   _____ g   _____ g

       length of solid   _____ cm   _____ cm

       width of solid   _____ cm   _____ cm

       thickness of solid   _____ cm   _____ cm

Show the calculation for the volume of the unknown for trial 1 (see Example Exercise 3).

       volume of solid   _____ cm^3 _____ cm^3

Show the calculation for the density of the unknown for trial 1 (see Example Exercise 3).

       Density of rectangular solid   _____ g/cm^3 _____ g/cm^3

         Average density of the solid   _____ g/cm^3

F. Thickness of Aluminum Foil

      length of foil   _____ cm

      width of foil   _____ cm

      mass of foil   _____ g

Show the calculation for the volume of the aluminum foil given the density of aluminum, $d = 2.70$ g/cm^3 (see Example Exercise 4).

      Volume of foil   _____ cm^3

Show the calculation for the thickness of the foil in centimeters.

      Thickness of foil   _____ cm

EXPERIMENT

DATE _____

NAME _____

SECTION _____

POSTLABORATORY ASSIGNMENT

1. Ether floats on water, and water floats on mercury, as shown in the following diagram.

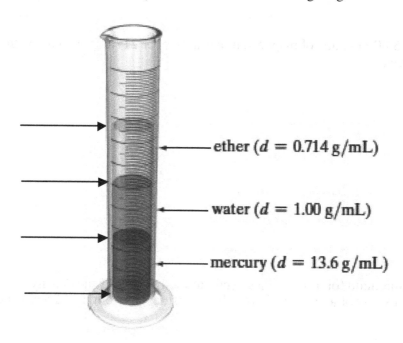

ether ($d = 0.714$ g/mL)

water ($d = 1.00$ g/mL)

mercury ($d = 13.6$ g/mL)

Indicate on the above diagram where each of the following would come to rest after being dropped into the glass cylinder.

(a) a glass marble ($d = 2.95$ g/cm^3)

(b) a platinum ring ($d = 21.45$ g/cm^3)

(c) a lump of coal ($d = 0.83$ g/cm^3)

(d) a champagne cork ($d = 0.19$ g/cm^3)

2. A 250-mL flask and stopper have a mass of 110.525 g. A 50.0-mL sample of gasoline is pipetted into the flask, giving a total mass of 146.770 g. Find the density of the gasoline.

_____

3. A piece of green jade has a mass of 26.123 g. If the sample of jade displaces 50.0 mL of water to 57.5 mL in a graduated cylinder, what is the density of the jade?

_____

4. A 5.00-cm cube of magnesium has a mass of 217.501 g. What is the density of magnesium metal?

_____

5. Aluminum foil is often incorrectly termed tin foil. If the density of tin is 7.28 g/cm^3, what is the thickness of a piece of tin foil that measures 5.70 cm by 4.25 cm and has a mass of 0.655 g?

_____

6. (optional) A silver sphere has a mass of 5.492 g and a diameter of 10.0 mm. What is the density of silver metal in grams per cubic centimeter? The volume of a sphere equals $4\pi r^3/3$, where π is 3.14, and r is the radius.

_____

ANSWERS TO PRELABORATORY ASSIGNMENTS

1. See the Glossary.
2. 0.799 g/mL
3. 54.0 mL, 62.5 mL
4. 1.2 g/mL
5. 5.40 cm, 4.25 cm
6. 8.90 g/cm^3
7. 0.00170 cm (1.70 x 10^{-3} cm)
8. • Wear safety goggles; be careful handling the 10-mL pipet.
   • Dispose of solvents in the organic waste container.

Physical Properties and Chemical Properties

OBJECTIVES

- To observe a demonstration of oxidation of a metal.
- To observe a demonstration of sublimation and deposition.
- To observe the appearance of several elements.
- To determine the boiling points of methyl alcohol and an unknown liquid.
- To determine whether a solid is *soluble* or *insoluble* in water.
- To determine whether a liquid is *soluble* or *insoluble* in water.
- To determine whether a substance is undergoing a *physical* or *chemical change*.
- To gain proficiency in determining a boiling point.

DISCUSSION

Chemists classify matter according to its physical and chemical properties. Matter can be classified as a mixture or a pure substance, depending upon its properties. A **heterogeneous mixture** has physical and chemical properties that vary within the sample. For example, combining sugar and salt gives a heterogeneous mixture because the properties of sugar and salt are different.

A **homogeneous mixture** has constant properties although the properties can vary from sample to sample. A homogeneous mixture may be a gaseous mixture, a solution, or an alloy. Examples include air, seawater, and brass, which is an alloy of the metals copper and zinc.

A pure **substance** is either a **compound** or an **element**. A pure substance has constant and predictable properties; examples include sodium chloride (compound), as well as sodium metal and chlorine gas (elements).

Water is a compound containing the elements hydrogen and oxygen. When electricity is passed through water, it decomposes into hydrogen gas and oxygen gas. Although hydrogen and oxygen are both colorless, odorless gases, they differ in their other physical and chemical properties. Figure 1 illustrates the overall relationship for the classification of matter.

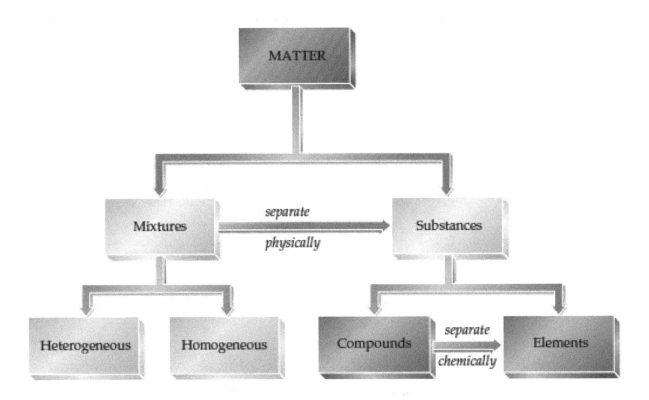

Figure 1 Classification of Matter Matter is classified as either a mixture or a pure substance. The properties of a *heterogeneous mixture* vary within the sample, but the properties of a *homogeneous mixture* are constant. A pure substance is either a *compound* or an *element*.

A **physical property** refers to a characteristic that can be observed without changing the composition of the substance. A partial list of important physical properties include: appearance, physical state (solid, liquid, or gas), density, malleability, ductility, conductivity of heat and electricity, melting point, boiling point, and solubility in water. A **chemical property** refers to a property that can only be observed during a chemical reaction. The chemical properties of oxygen gas include its ability to react with most metals and nonmetals. On the other hand, helium is an inert gas and does not react with other elements.

In this experiment, we will observe a **physical change** as a substance undergoes a change in physical state, a temporary change in color, or a simple change in volume when two solutions are added together. We will observe a **chemical change** when a substance releases a gas, undergoes a permanent change in color, or forms an insoluble substance when two solutions are added together. An antacid tablet fizzing in water, a banana changing color from green to yellow, and the formation of an insoluble "bathtub ring," are all familiar and practical examples of a chemical change.

EQUIPMENT and CHEMICALS

- ring stand & ring
- wire gauze
- hotplate (optional)
- 400-mL beaker
- 16 x 150 mm test tube
- boiling chip
- 110 °C thermometer
- split cork
- 13 x 100 mm test tubes (6) & test tube rack
- test tube holder
- test tube brush
- wash bottle with distilled water

- copper wire, heavy gauge Cu
- iodine, solid crystals I_2
- small vials with samples of cobalt, hydrogen, magnesium, manganese, neon, oxygen, silicon, sulfur, tin, zinc
- methyl alcohol, CH_3OH
- boiling point unknowns
- copper(II) sulfate, $CuSO_4 \cdot 5H_2O$
- calcium carbonate crystals, $CaCO_3$
- amyl alcohol (pentanol), $C_5H_{11}OH$
- ammonium bicarbonate, solid NH_4HCO_3
- potassium bicarbonate, solid $KHCO_3$
- sodium carbonate solution, 0.5 M Na_2CO_3
- sodium sulfate solution, 0.1 M Na_2SO_4
- dilute hydrochloric acid, 6 M HCl
- calcium nitrate solution, 0.1 M $Ca(NO_3)_2$
- copper(II) nitrate solution, 0.1 M $Cu(NO_3)_2$
- ammonium hydroxide solution, 6 M NH_4OH

PROCEDURE

A. Instructor Demonstrations

1. *Heating Copper Wire*

   Show a piece of copper wire to the class. Hold the wire with crucible tongs and heat until the wire is red hot. Allow the wire to cool and show the class the wire after heating. Classify the observation as a *physical change* or *chemical change*.

   Note: If students suggest the copper wire is covered with carbon from the burner flame (i.e., a physical change), the instructor can quickly disprove this by placing a piece of charcoal in one test tube and the copper wire in a second test tube. After adding hydrochloric acid to each test tube, students can observe a change in one test tube and no change in the other.

RECYCLE
Chemical
Waste

2. *Heating Iodine Crystals*

   Put 3 small crystals of iodine in a dry 250-mL beaker. Cover the beaker using an evaporating dish containing ice. Support the beaker on a ring stand (see Figure 2) and gently heat the crystals until all the iodine vaporizes. Using crucible tongs to hold the hot evaporating dish, show the class the bottom of the evaporating dish and classify the observation as a *physical change* or *chemical change*.

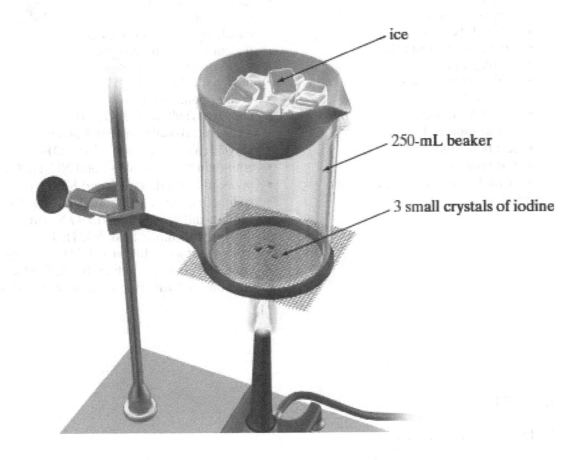

ice

250-mL beaker

3 small crystals of iodine

Figure 2 Apparatus for Sublimation/Deposition Gently heat a few crystals of iodine in the beaker. The iodine crystals undergo *sublimation*, which in turn undergoes *deposition* on the bottom of the evaporating dish.

B. Observation of Elements

Observe vials of the following elements and record your observations in the Data Table. Classify each element as a metal, semimetal, or nonmetal.

(a) cobalt   (b) hydrogen
(c) magnesium   (d) manganese
(e) neon   (f) oxygen
(g) silicon   (h) sulfur
(i) tin   (j) zinc

C. Physical Properties

1. *Boiling Point*
   (a) Support a 400-mL beaker on a ring stand as shown in Figure 3. Add 300 mL of distilled water to the beaker, bring to a boil, and shut off the burner. Add a boiling chip and 20 drops of methyl alcohol into a 16 x 150 mm test tube. Place the test tube in the hot water and suspend a thermometer about 1 cm above the liquid.

   (b) After the alcohol begins to boil in the test tube, record the boiling point (± 0.5°C) when alcohol drips from the tip of the thermometer every few seconds.

   Caution: Methyl alcohol is flammable; keep away from flames.

   (c) Record the number of an unknown liquid, and determine the boiling point of the liquid (± 0.5°C) as above.

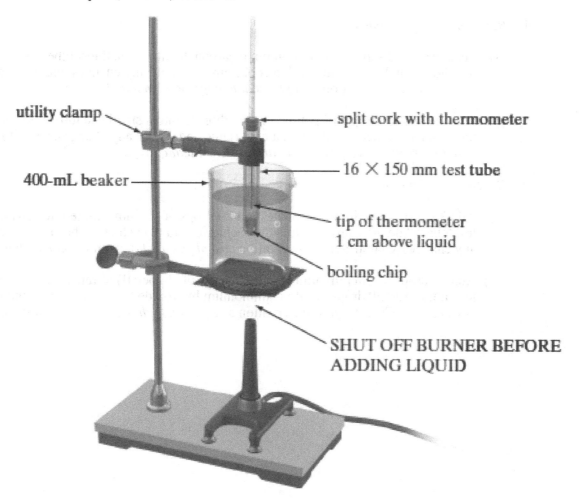

RECYCLE
Chemical
Waste

Figure 3 Boiling Point Apparatus The boiling point is recorded as vapor condenses on the tip of the thermometer and drips every 2 or 3 seconds.

Alternate Apparatus: If hotplates are available, the Instructor may wish to use a hotplate rather than the laboratory burner. Using a hotplate, bring the water in the beaker to a boil, and turn off the hotplate.

2. *Solubility of a Solid in Water*

Add 20 drops of distilled water into two test tubes. Drop a copper sulfate crystal into one test tube, and a calcium carbonate crystal into the other. Shake the test tubes briefly to observe solubility. State whether each solid is *soluble* or *insoluble* in water.

3. *Solubility of a Liquid in Water*

Add 20 drops of distilled water in two test tubes. Add a few drops of methyl alcohol to one test tube, and amyl alcohol to the other. Shake the test tubes briefly to mix the liquids. State whether each liquid is *soluble* or *insoluble* in water.

D. Chemical Properties

1. *Reactions of Compounds*

RECYCLE
Chemical
Waste

(a) Put a pea-sized sample of ammonium bicarbonate into a small test tube. Use a test tube holder and heat gently with a cool flame and note any changes, including odor. Classify your observation as a *physical change* or a *chemical change*.

(b) Put a pea-sized sample of potassium bicarbonate into a small test tube. Use a test tube holder and heat gently with a cool flame and record any changes. Classify your observation as a *physical change* or *chemical change*.

2. *Reactions of Solutions*

(a) Add 20 drops of sodium carbonate, and 20 drops of sodium sulfate into separate test tubes. Add 20 drops of dilute hydrochloric acid to each test tube, and record any changes. Classify your observation as a *physical change* or *chemical change*.

(b) Add 20 drops of calcium nitrate, and 20 drops of copper(II) nitrate into separate test tubes. Add 20 drops of dilute ammonium hydroxide to each test tube, and note any changes. Classify your observation as a *physical change* or *chemical change*.

EXPERIMENT   NAME _____

DATE _____   SECTION _____

PRELABORATORY ASSIGNMENT*

1. Provide the key term that corresponds to each of the following definitions.

    _____ (a) matter having an indefinite composition and properties that can vary within the sample

    _____ (b) matter having a definite composition but properties that can vary from sample to sample; examples include alloys and solutions

    _____ (c) matter having constant composition with definite and predictable properties

    _____ (d) a pure substance that can be broken down into two or more simpler substances by chemical reaction

    _____ (e) a pure substance that cannot be broken down any further by chemical reaction

    _____ (f) a characteristic of the substance that can be observed without changing its chemical formula

    _____ (g) a characteristic of a substance that cannot be observed without changing its chemical formula

    _____ (h) a modification of a substance that does not alter its chemical composition

    _____ (i) a modification of a substance that alters its chemical composition

    _____ (j) an insoluble solid substance produced from a reaction in aqueous solution

    Key Terms: chemical change, chemical property, compound, element, heterogeneous mixture, homogeneous mixture, physical change, physical property, precipitate, substance

2. Classify the following characteristics as a physical (*phys*) or chemical (*chem*) property.

(a)	physical state	(b)	density
(c)	melting point	(d)	hardness
(e)	appearance	(f)	reactivity
(g)	solubility	(h)	conductivity

3. Classify the following observations as a physical (*phys*) or chemical (*chem*) change.

(a)	candle burning	(b)	wax melting
(c)	alcohol vaporizing	(d)	antacid fizzing in water
(e)	apple turning brown	(f)	steam condensing on a mirror
(g)	fire releasing heat	(h)	fireworks releasing light

_____

* Answers at the end of the experiment.

4. What is the purpose of the boiling chip when determining the boiling point of a liquid?

5. What experimental observations indicate a chemical change is taking place?

6. What experimental observations indicate a gas is being released?

7. What safety precautions must be observed in this experiment?

EXPERIMENT

NAME _____

DATE _____

SECTION _____

DATA TABLE

A. Instructor Demonstrations

Procedure	Physical Change/ Observation	Chemical Change
1. Heating Copper Wire		
2. Heating Iodine Crystals		

RECYCLE
Chemical
Waste

B. Observation of Elements

Element	Symbol	Physical State	Color	Metal/Semimetal/ Nonmetal
cobalt				
hydrogen				
magnesium				
manganese				
neon				
oxygen				
silicon				
sulfur				
tin				
zinc				

41

C. Physical Properties

    1. *Boiling Point*

        Bp of methyl alcohol (65.0°C)   _____ °C

        Bp of **UNKNOWN #**_____   _____ °C

    2. *Solubility of a Solid in Water*

        copper sulfate crystal and water   _____

        calcium carbonate crystal and water   _____

    3. *Solubility of a Liquid in Water*

        methyl alcohol (methanol) and water   _____

        amyl alcohol (pentanol) and water   _____

D. Chemical Properties

Procedure	Observation	Physical Change/ Chemical Change
1. *Reactions of Compounds*		
(a) ammonium bicarbonate + heat		
(b) potassium bicarbonate + heat		
2. *Reactions of Solutions*		
(a) sodium carbonate + hydrochloric acid		
sodium sulfate + hydrochloric acid		
(b) calcium nitrate + ammonium hydroxide		
copper(II) nitrate + ammonium hydroxide		

RECYCLE
Chemical
Waste

EXPERIMENT   NAME   _____

DATE _____   SECTION   _____

POSTLABORATORY ASSIGNMENT

1. State whether the following properties are more typical of a *metal* or a *nonmetal* element.

   (a)   silver solid   _____   (b)   yellow solid   _____

   (c)   ductile solid   _____   (d)   colorless gas   _____

   (e)   high melting point   _____   (f)   poor conductor   _____

2. Classify each of the following as an example of an *element, compound, homogeneous mixture,* or *heterogeneous mixture*.

   (a)   copper, Cu   _____   (b)   copper alloy   _____

   (c)   copper oxide, CuO   _____   (d)   copper ore   _____

3. Classify the following as a physical property (*phys*) or a chemical property (*chem*).

   (a)   Copper metal has a red-orange metallic luster.   _____

   (b)   Copper metal has a density of 8.94 g/cm^3.   _____

   (c)   Copper metal and chlorine gas produce $CuCl_2$.   _____

   (d)   Copper metal has a melting point of 1084 °C.   _____

   (e)   Copper metal conducts electricity.   _____

   (f)   Copper metal and acid give no reaction.   _____

4. Classify the following as a physical change (*phys*) or a chemical change (*chem*).

   (a)   Silver tarnishes when exposed to air.   _____

   (b)   Baking soda fizzes when added to vinegar.   _____

   (c)   Alcohol dissolves when added to water.   _____

   (d)   White phosphorus glows when exposed to air.   _____

   (e)   Soap and tap water form an insoluble "bathtub ring,"   _____

   (f)   Water evaporates from a lake.   _____

5. Refer to the *Handbook of Chemistry and Physics, The Elements*, to research the density, melting point, and boiling point for the following elements.

Name	density ($g \cdot cm^{-3}$)	mp (°C)	bp (°C)
Cobalt	_____	_____	_____
Magnesium	_____	_____	_____
Manganese	_____	_____	_____
Silicon	_____	_____	_____
Zinc	_____	_____	_____

6. (optional) Go online to Wikipedia at www.wikipedia.org to research the density, melting point, and boiling point for the following elements.

Name	density ($g \cdot cm^{-3}$)	mp (°C)	bp (°C)
Cobalt	_____	_____	_____
Magnesium	_____	_____	_____
Manganese	_____	_____	_____
Silicon	_____	_____	_____
Zinc	_____	_____	_____

ANSWERS TO PRELABORATORY ASSIGNMENTS

1. See the Glossary.
2. (a) phys; (b) phys; (c) phys; (d) phys; (e) phys; (f) chem; (g) phys; (h) phys
3. (a) chem; (b) phys; (c) phys; (d) chem; (e) chem; (f) phys; (g) chem; (h) chem
4. The boiling chip prevents "bumping" that can eject flammable liquid from the test tube.
5. All of the following indicate a chemical change:
   (1) a solution releases gas bubbles; (2) a solution forms an insoluble solid; (3) a solution undergoes a permanent color change; (4) a solution releases or absorbs energy.
6. A gas is indicated if there is fizzing, bubbling, or an odor is observed.
7. • Wear safety goggles; keep flammable organic liquids away from a burner flame.
   • Handle the thermometer carefully, as it is easily broken and can cause cuts.
     (Report a broken thermometer immediately to the Instructor.)
   • Dispose of chemical waste in the designated container.

Identifying Cations in Solution

OBJECTIVES

- To observe the chemical behavior of barium, calcium, and magnesium ions.
- To analyze an unknown solution for one or more of the following cations: Ba^{2+}, Ca^{2+}, and Mg^{2+}.
- To develop the following laboratory skills: centrifuging, flame testing, and using litmus paper.

DISCUSSION

Qualitative analysis is a systematic procedure for the separation and identification of ions present in an unknown solution. Cation analysis involves the separation and identification of each positively charged **cation** present in a sample.

If we have an **aqueous solution** containing different cations, it is possible to select a reagent that will form a **precipitate** with one of the cations, but not with the others. We can then use a **centrifuge** to separate the solid particles of precipitate from the aqueous solution. Thus, we separate the cation in the precipitate from the other cations in the original aqueous solution.

For example, we can separate the cations in a solution containing Ba^{2+}, Ca^{2+}, and Mg^{2+}, using ammonium sulfate. The sulfate ion, SO_4^{2-}, precipitates Ba^{2+}, but gives no reaction with either Ca^{2+} or Mg^{2+} cations (see Figure 1).

From Experiment 8 of *Laboratory Manual to Accompany Introductory Chemistry: Concepts and Critical Thinking*, Sixth Edition. Charles H. Corwin.

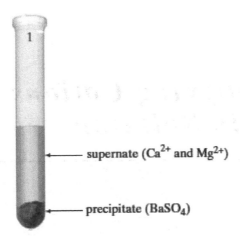

Figure 1 Precipitation of BaSO₄ The reaction of Ba^{2+} and SO_4^{2-} gives $BaSO_4$ precipitate. There is *no reaction* between Ca^{2+} and SO_4^{2-}, or Mg^{2+} and SO_4^{2-}, because $CaSO_4$ and $MgSO_4$ are both soluble.

When barium ions and sulfate ions are in a solution, a white precipitate forms because barium sulfate, $BaSO_4$, is insoluble. If calcium and sulfate ions are in a solution, no precipitate forms because calcium sulfate, $CaSO_4$, is soluble. Similarly, no precipitate forms with magnesium and sulfate ions because magnesium sulfate, $MgSO_4$, is soluble.

A **flame test** can be used to confirm the presence of an ion. A flame test is performed by dipping a wire into a solution and holding the wire in a flame while observing the color produced (Figure 2). Different ions produce different colored flames. For example, sodium ions give an orange-yellow flame. Since sodium is usually present as an impurity, flame tests are invariably contaminated by the orange-yellow sodium flame.

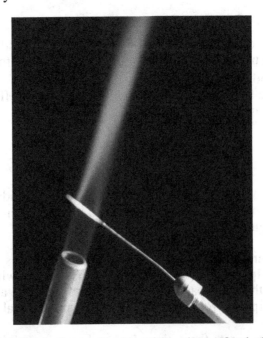

Figure 2 Flame-Test Technique A wire with a drop of solution in the coiled tip is placed in a hot burner flame. A brief, yellow-green flame indicates barium; and a brick-red flame indicates calcium.

Litmus paper can be used to determine whether a solution is acidic or basic. A glass stirring rod is placed in the solution and touched to the litmus paper. Acidic solutions make a *red spot* on blue litmus paper. Basic solutions make a **blue spot** on red litmus paper (Figure 3).

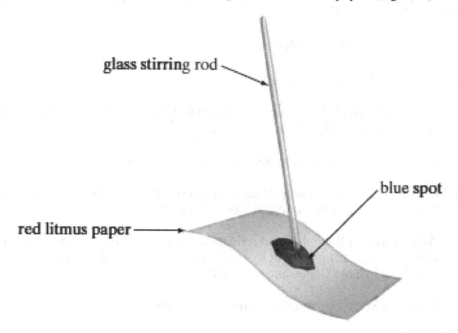

Figure 3 Litmus Paper Test for a Basic Solution A glass stirring rod is placed in a solution and touched to red litmus paper. A **blue spot** appears if the solution is basic. If there is no change, the solution is neutral or acidic.

In this experiment, you will identify Ba^{2+}, Ca^{2+}, and Mg^{2+}. First, a known solution containing all three cations will be analyzed to develop the necessary techniques. Second, an unknown solution containing one or more cations will be analyzed to determine the cations present.

EQUIPMENT and CHEMICALS

- 13 x 100 mm test tubes (3) & test tube rack
- thin glass stirring rod
- wash bottle with distilled water
- test tube brush
- red litmus paper
- flame-test wire

- known cation solution (Ba^{2+}, Ca^{2+}, and Mg^{2+} as 0.1 M $BaCl_2$, $CaCl_2$, $MgCl_2$)

- ammonium sulfate solution, 0.1 M $(NH_4)_2SO_4$
- ammonium oxalate solution, 0.1 M $(NH_4)_2C_2O_4$
- sodium hydrogen phosphate, 0.1 M Na_2HPO_4
- magnesium indicator (0.1 g *para*-nitrobenzene-azo-resorcinol in 1 L of 0.025 M NaOH)
- dilute hydrochloric acid, 6 M HCl
- dilute sodium hydroxide, 6 M NaOH

- unknown cation solutions (Ba^{2+}, Ca^{2+}, and/or Mg^{2+} as 0.1 M $BaCl_2$, $CaCl_2$, $MgCl_2$)

PROCEDURE

General Directions: Clean three test tubes and a glass stirring rod with distilled water. Label the test tubes #1, #2, and #3.

A. Analysis of a Known Cation Solution

1. *Identification of Ba^{2+} in a Known Solution*

    (a) Place 10 drops of the known solution in test tube #1. Add 20 drops of ammonium sulfate, $(NH_4)_2SO_4$, and mix with a glass stirring rod.

    Note: A white precipitate suggests Ba^{2+} is present.

    (b) Centrifuge, and add 1 drop of ammonium sulfate to verify complete precipitation. Pour off the supernate into test tube #2, and save for Step 2.

    (c) Add 5 drops of dilute hydrochloric acid, HCl, to test tube #1, and stir thoroughly. Clean a flame-test wire with hydrochloric acid and dip it into the solution. Place the wire loop in a hot flame, and record the color.

    Note: A green flame test confirms Ba^{2+} is present.

2. *Identification of Ca^{2+} in a Known Solution*

    RECYCLE
    Chemical
    Waste

    (a) Add 10 drops of ammonium oxalate, $(NH_4)_2C_2O_4$, to the solution in test tube #2.

    Note: A white precipitate suggests Ca^{2+} is present.

    (b) Centrifuge, and add 1 drop of ammonium oxalate to verify complete precipitation. Pour off the supernate into test tube #3, and save for Step 3.

    (c) Add 5 drops of dilute hydrochloric acid to test tube #2, and stir thoroughly. Clean a flame-test wire with dilute HCl and dip the wire into the solution. Place the wire loop in a hot flame, and record the color.

    Note: A brick-red flame test confirms Ca^{2+} is present.

3. *Identification of Mg^{2+} in a Known Solution*

    (a) Add 10 drops of sodium hydrogen phosphate, Na_2HPO_4, to the solution in test tube #3. Add 1 drop of sodium hydroxide, NaOH, and stir with a glass rod.

    Note: A white precipitate suggests Mg^{2+} is present.

    (b) Centrifuge, and discard the supernate.

    (c) Dissolve the precipitate with dilute hydrochloric acid in test tube #3. Add 5 drops of magnesium indicator. Add sodium hydroxide, NaOH, dropwise until the solution turns red litmus paper blue. Centrifuge the precipitate.

    Note: A blue gel precipitate confirms Mg^{2+} is present.

B. Analysis of an Unknown Cation Solution

1. *Identification of Ba^{2+} in an Unknown Solution*

   (a) Place 10 drops of unknown solution in test tube #1. Add 20 drops of ammonium sulfate, $(NH_4)_2SO_4$, and stir with a glass rod.

   Note: If there is no precipitate, Ba^{2+} is absent. Go directly to Step 2.

   (b) Centrifuge, and then test for completeness of precipitation by adding 1 drop of ammonium sulfate. Pour off the supernate into test tube #2, and save for Step 2.

   (c) Add 5 drops of dilute hydrochloric acid, HCl, to test tube #1 and stir thoroughly. Clean a flame-test wire with dilute HCl, and dip the wire into the solution. Place the wire loop in a hot flame, and record the color.

   Note: A green flame test confirms Ba^{2+} is present.

2. *Identification of Ca^{2+} in an Unknown Solution*

   (a) Add 10 drops of ammonium oxalate, $(NH_4)_2C_2O_4$, to the solution in test tube #2.

   Note: If there is no precipitate, Ca^{2+} is absent. Go directly to Step 3.

   (b) Centrifuge, and then test for completeness of precipitation by adding 1 drop of ammonium oxalate. Pour off the supernate into test tube #3, and save for Step 3.

RECYCLE
Chemical
Waste

   (c) Add 5 drops of dilute hydrochloric acid, HCl, to test tube #2 and stir thoroughly. Clean a flame-test wire with dilute HCl, and dip the wire into the solution. Place the wire loop in a hot flame, and record the color.

   Note: A brick-red flame test confirms Ca^{2+} is present.

3. *Identification of Mg^{2+} in an Unknown Solution*

   (a) Add 10 drops of sodium hydrogen phosphate, Na_2HPO_4, to the solution in test tube #3. Add 1 drop of sodium hydroxide, NaOH, and stir with a glass rod.

   Note: If there is no precipitate, Mg^{2+} is absent.

   (b) Centrifuge, and discard the supernate.

   (c) Dissolve the precipitate with dilute hydrochloric acid in test tube #3. Add 5 drops of magnesium indicator. Add sodium hydroxide, NaOH, dropwise until the solution turns red litmus paper blue. Centrifuge the precipitate.

   Note: A blue gel precipitate confirms Mg^{2+} is present.

4. Based on the observations in steps 1–3, identify the cation(s) present in the unknown solution.

EXPERIMENT   NAME   _____

DATE   _____   SECTION   _____

PRELABORATORY ASSIGNMENT*

1. Provide the key term that corresponds to each of the following definitions.

   _____ (a)   any positively charged ion

   _____ b)   a systematic procedure for the separation and identification of cations, or other substances present in a sample

   _____ (c)   a solution of a substance dissolved in water

   _____ (d)   an insoluble solid substance produced from a reaction in aqueous solution

   _____ (e)   an instrument that spins test tubes to separate a precipitate from solution

   _____ (f)   the solution above a precipitate after insoluble particles are centrifuged from solution

   _____ (g)   the process of pouring a liquid from one container into another

   _____ (h)   a means of identifying an ion by observing the characteristic color it emits when placed in a hot flame

      Key Terms: aqueous solution, cation, centrifuge, decant, flame test, precipitate (ppt), qualitative analysis, supernate

2. Which three cations are investigated in this experiment? (Refer to **Figure 1**.)

3. Where is the end of the wire placed when performing a flame test? (Refer to **Figure 2**.)

4. What color is the spot on red litmus paper when testing a basic solution? (Refer to **Figure 3**.)

5. Refer to the **Data Table** to answer the following.

   (a)   Which cation is confirmed in test tube #1 by a *yellow-green* flame test?   _____

   (b)   Which cation is confirmed in test tube #2 by a *brick-red* flame test?   _____

   (c)   Which cation is confirmed in test tube #3 by a *blue "lake"* precipitate?   _____

_____

* Answers at the end of the experiment.

6. Why is it necessary to use distilled water throughout the experiment?

7. Refer to the **Data Table** to determine which cations (Ba^{2+}, Ca^{2+}, Mg^{2+}) are present and absent in an unknown solution given the following observations.

   - The unknown solution in test tube #1 plus $(NH_4)_2SO_4$ gives a white precipitate.
   - The supernate in test tube #1 is poured into test tube #2.
   - The white precipitate in test tube #1 gives a green flame test.
   - The solution in test tube #2 plus $(NH_4)_2C_2O_4$ gives a white precipitate.
   - The white precipitate in test tube #2 gives a brick-red flame test.
   - The supernate in test tube #2 is poured into test tube #3.
   - The solution in test tube #3 plus Na_2HPO_4 and NaOH gives a white precipitate.
   - The white precipitate in test tube #3 dissolves in HCl; magnesium indicator and NaOH is added until the solution tests basic. A blue gel is observed at the bottom of the test tube.

   Cation(s) **present** _____   Cation(s) **absent** _____

8. Refer to the **Data Table** to determine which cations (Ba^{2+}, Ca^{2+}, Mg^{2+}) are present and absent in an unknown solution given the following observations.

   - The unknown solution in test tube #1 plus $(NH_4)_2SO_4$ gives no reaction.
   - The solution in test tube #1 is poured into test tube #2.
   - The solution in test tube #2 plus $(NH_4)_2C_2O_4$ gives no reaction.
   - The solution in test tube #2 is poured into test tube #3.
   - The solution in test tube #3 plus Na_2HPO_4 and NaOH gives a white precipitate.
   - The white precipitate in test tube #3 dissolves in HCl; magnesium indicator and NaOH is added until the solution tests basic. A blue gel is observed at the bottom of the test tube.

   Cation(s) **present** _____   Cation(s) **absent** _____

9. What safety precautions should be taken while performing this experiment?

EXPERIMENT   NAME _____

DATE _____   SECTION _____

DATA TABLE

A. Analysis of a Known Cation Solution

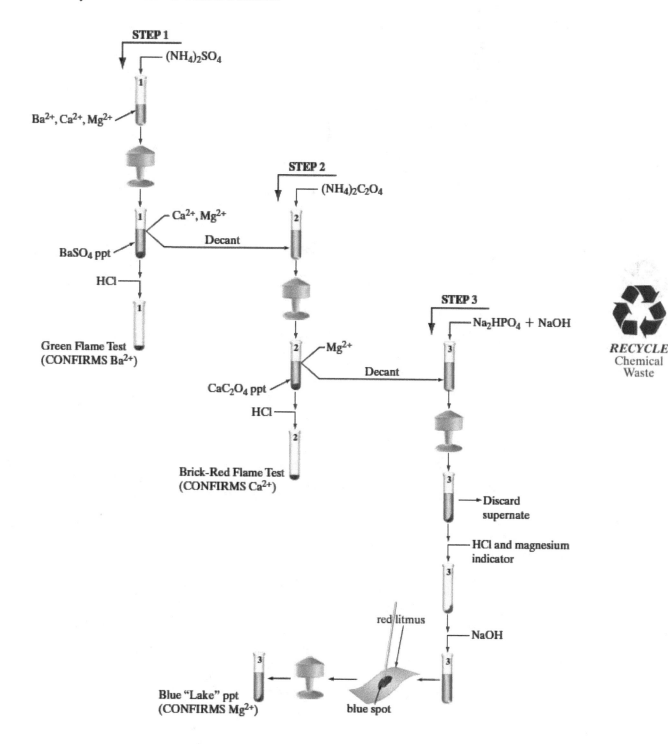

B. Analysis of an Unknown Cation Solution

UNKNOWN # _____

Cation(s) **present** _____

Cation(s) **absent** _____

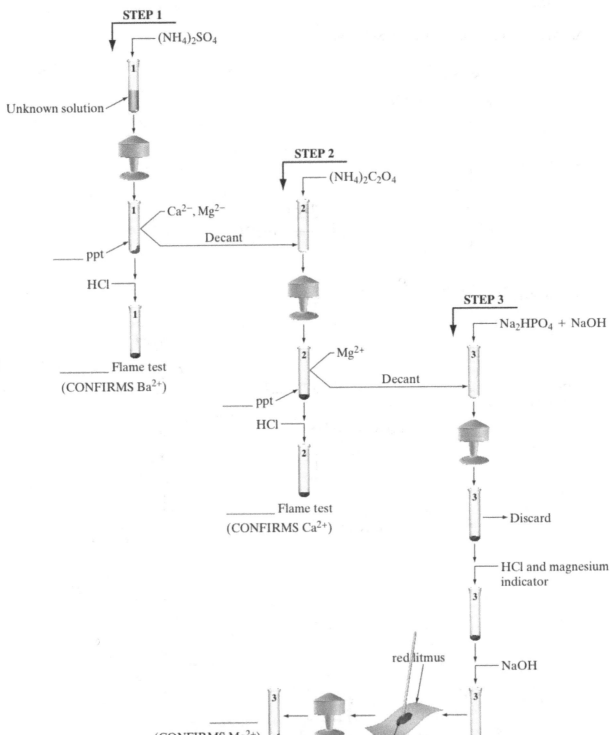

STEP 1

$(NH_4)_2SO_4$

Unknown solution

STEP 2

$(NH_4)_2C_2O_4$

Ca^{2-}, Mg^{2-}

Decant

ppt

HCl

_____ Flame test
(CONFIRMS Ba^{2+})

STEP 3

Na_2HPO_4 + NaOH

Mg^{2+}

Decant

ppt

HCl

_____ Flame test
(CONFIRMS Ca^{2+})

→ Discard

HCl and magnesium
indicator

NaOH

red litmus

_____ spot

(CONFIRMS Mg^{2+})

RECYCLE
Chemical
Waste

EXPERIMENT   NAME _____

DATE _____   SECTION _____

POSTLABORATORY ASSIGNMENT

1. Which cations are present and absent in an unknown solution given the following observations?

    - The unknown solution in test tube #1 plus $(NH_4)_2SO_4$ gives a white precipitate.
    - The supernate in test tube #1 is poured into test tube #2.
    - The white precipitate in test tube #1 gives a green flame test.
    - The solution in test tube #2 plus $(NH_4)_2C_2O_4$ gives a white precipitate.
    - The white precipitate in test tube #2 gives a brick-red flame test.
    - The supernate in test tube #2 is poured into test tube #3.
    - The solution in test tube #3 plus Na_2HPO_4 and NaOH gives no reaction.

    Cation(s) **present** _____   Cation(s) **absent** _____

2. Which cations are present and absent in an unknown solution given the following observations?

    - The unknown solution in test tube #1 plus $(NH_4)_2SO_4$ gives no reaction.
    - The solution in test tube #1 is poured into test tube #2.
    - The solution in test tube #2 plus $(NH_4)_2C_2O_4$ gives a white precipitate.
    - The white precipitate in test tube #2 gives a brick-red flame test.
    - The supernate in test tube #2 is poured into test tube #3.
    - The solution in test tube #3 plus Na_2HPO_4 and NaOH gives a white precipitate.
    - The white precipitate in test tube #3 dissolves in HCl; magnesium indicator and NaOH is added until the solution tests basic. A blue gel is observed at the bottom of the test tube.

    Cation(s) **present** _____   Cation(s) **absent** _____

3. Write the **Stock system** name for the following cations.

    (a) Cu^+ _____   (b) Cu^{2+} _____

    (c) Fe^{2+} _____   (d) Fe^{3+} _____

    (e) Sn^{2+} _____   (f) Sn^{4+} _____

4. Write the **Latin system** name for the following cations.

    (a) Cu^+ _____   (b) Cu^{2+} _____

    (c) Fe^{2+} _____   (d) Fe^{3+} _____

    (e) Sn^{2+} _____   (f) Sn^{4+} _____

5. Complete the table below as shown by the example. Combine the ions into a correct formula, and name the compound.

	NO_3^-	SO_4^{2-}	PO_4^{3-}
Ba^{2+}	$Ba(NO_3)_2$ *barium nitrate*		
Ca^{2+}			
Mg^{2+}			

6. (optional) Complete the table below as shown by the example. Combine the ions into a correct formula, and name the compound.

	nitrite ion	sulfite ion	phosphite ion
mercury(II) ion	$Hg(NO_2)_2$ *mercury(II) nitrite*		
iron(III) ion			
lead(IV) ion			

ANSWERS TO PRELABORATORY ASSIGNMENTS

1. See the Glossary.
2. Ba^{2+}, Ca^{2+}, and Mg^{2+}
3. When performing a flame test, the end of the wire is placed at the tip of the burner flame.
4. A blue spot indicates a basic solution. If the spot is red, add a few more drops of NaOH.
5. (a) Ba^{2+}; (b) Ca^{2+}; and (c) Mg^{2+}
6. Tap water contains ions that can interfere with the analysis.
7. All three cations (Ba^{2+}, Ca^{2+}, and Mg^{2+}) are present.
8. Mg^{2+} is present; Ba^{2+} and Ca^{2+} are absent.
9. • Wear safety goggles; be careful when using the burner and performing a flame test.
   • Avoid contact with HCl and NaOH. If contacted, wash immediately with water.
   • Balance the centrifuge before operating.
   • Dispose of chemical waste in the designated container.

Identifying Anions in Solution

OBJECTIVES

- To observe the chemical behavior of iodide, chloride, and sulfate ions.
- To analyze an unknown solution for one or more of the following anions:
  I^-, Cl^-, and SO_4^{2-}.
- To develop the following laboratory skills: centrifuging, washing a precipitate, and using litmus paper.

DISCUSSION

Qualitative analysis is a systematic procedure for the separation and identification of ions present in an unknown solution. Anion analysis involves the separation and identification of each negatively charged **anion** present in a sample.

If we have an **aqueous solution** containing different anions, it is possible to select a reagent that will form a **precipitate** with one of the anions, but not with the others. We can then use a **centrifuge** to separate the solid particles of precipitate from the aqueous solution. Thus, we separate the anion in the precipitate from the other anions in the original aqueous solution.

For example, we can separate the anions in a solution containing I^-, Cl^-, and SO_4^{2-}, using silver nitrate. The silver ion, Ag^+, precipitates I^- and Cl^-, but gives no reaction with the SO_4^{2-} anion (see Figure 1).

From Experiment 9 of *Laboratory Manual to Accompany Introductory Chemistry: Concepts and Critical Thinking*, Sixth Edition. Charles H. Corwin. Copyright © 2013 by Pearson Education, Inc. All rights reserved.

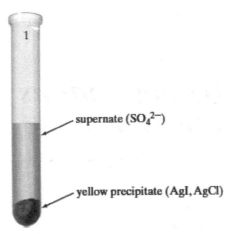

Figure 1 Precipitation of AgI and AgCl The reaction of Ag and I gives AgI
precipitate; Ag+ and Cl− gives AgCl precipitate.. There is *no reaction* between
Ag+ and SO_4^{2-} because Ag_2SO_4 is soluble.

When silver ions and iodide ions are in a solution, a yellow precipitate forms because silver
iodide, AgI, is insoluble. Similarly, silver ions and chloride ions in a solution give a white precipitate
of silver chloride, AgCl. If silver ions and sulfate ions are in a solution, no precipitate forms because
silver sulfate, Ag_2SO_4, is soluble.

In this experiment, you will identify I −, Cl−, and SO_4^{2-}. First, a known solution containing
all three anions will be analyzed to develop the necessary techniques. Second, an unknown solution
containing one or more anions will be analyzed to determine the anions present.

Litmus paper can be used to determine whether a solution is acidic or basic. A glass stirring
rod is placed in the solution and touched to the litmus paper. Basic solutions make a *blue spot* on
red litmus paper. Acidic solutions make a ***red spot*** on blue litmus paper (Figure 2).

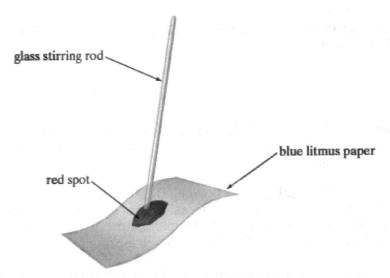

Figure 2 Litmus Paper Test for an Acidic Solution A glass stirring rod is
placed in a solution and touched to blue litmus paper. A ***red spot*** appears if the
solution is acidic. If there is no change, the solution is neutral or basic.

EQUIPMENT and CHEMICALS

- 13 x 100 mm test tubes (3)
  & test tube rack
- thin glass stirring rod
- wash bottle with distilled water
- centrifuge
- blue litmus paper

- silver nitrate solution,
  0.1 M AgNO$_3$
- dilute ammonium hydroxide,
  6 M NH$_4$OH
- dilute nitric acid, 6 M HNO$_3$
- barium nitrate solution,
  0.1 M Ba(NO$_3$)$_2$

- known anion solution
  (I$^-$, Cl$^-$, and SO$_4{}^{2-}$ as
  0.1 M NaI, NaCl, Na$_2$SO$_4$)

- unknown anion solutions
  (I$^-$, Cl$^-$, and/or SO$_4{}^{2-}$ as
  0.1 M NaI, NaCl, Na$_2$SO$_4$)

PROCEDURE

General Directions: Clean three test tubes and a glass stirring rod with distilled water. Label the test tubes #1, #2, and #3.

A. Analysis of a Known Anion Solution

1. *Identification of I$^-$ in a Known Solution*

   (a) Place 10 drops of the known solution in test tube #1. Add 20 drops of silver nitrate, AgNO$_3$, and mix with a glass stirring rod.

   Note: A yellow precipitate, AgI, suggests I$^-$ is present.

   (b) Centrifuge the precipitate. Pour the supernate into test tube #3 and save for Step 3.

   RECYCLE Chemical Waste

   (c) Add 10 drops of dilute ammonium hydroxide, NH$_4$OH, to test tube #1 and stir thoroughly with a glass rod. Centrifuge the precipitate. Pour the supernate into test tube #2 and save for Step 2.

   Note: A yellow precipitate, AgI, confirms I$^-$ is present.
   (*If the precipitate is white, add 10 drops of water and stir with a glass rod.*)

2. *Identification of Cl$^-$ in a Known Solution*

   Add dilute nitric acid, HNO$_3$, dropwise into test tube #2 until the solution turns blue litmus paper red. Centrifuge the precipitate.

   Note: A white precipitate, AgCl, confirms Cl$^-$ is present.
   (*If the precipitate is yellow, it contains AgI particles from test tube #1.*)

3. *Identification of SO_4^{2-} in a Known Solution*

   Add 10 drops of barium nitrate, $Ba(NO_3)_2$, to the solution in test tube #3. Centrifuge the precipitate.

   Note: A white precipitate, $BaSO_4$, confirms SO_4^{2-} is present.
   (*If the precipitate is yellow, it contains AgI particles from test tube #1.*)

B. Analysis of an Unknown Anion Solution

   1. *Identification of I^- in an Unknown Solution*

      (a) Place 10 drops of unknown solution in test tube #1. Add 20 drops of silver nitrate, $AgNO_3$, and stir with a glass rod.

         Note: If there is no precipitate, I^- and Cl^- are absent. Go directly to Step 3.

      (b) Centrifuge the precipitate. Pour the supernate into test tube #3, and save for Step 3.

      (c) Add 10 drops of dilute ammonium hydroxide, NH_4OH, to test tube #1, and stir thoroughly with a glass rod. Centrifuge the precipitate. Pour the supernate into test tube #2, and save for Step 2.

         Note: If there is no precipitate, I^- is absent. Go directly to Step 2.

   2. *Identification of Cl^- in an Unknown Solution*

      Add dilute nitric acid, HNO_3, dropwise to test tube #2 until the solution turns blue litmus paper red. Centrifuge the precipitate.

      Note: If there is no precipitate, Cl^- is absent. Go directly to Step 3.

   3. *Identification of SO_4^{2-} in an Unknown Solution*

      Add 10 drops of barium nitrate, $Ba(NO_3)_2$, to the solution in test tube #3. Centrifuge the precipitate.

      Note: If there is no precipitate, SO_4^{2-} is absent.

   4. Based on the observations in steps 1–3, identify the anion(s) present in the unknown solution.

RECYCLE
Chemical
Waste

EXPERIMENT   NAME   _____

DATE _____   SECTION   _____

PRELABORATORY ASSIGNMENT*

1. Provide the key term that corresponds to each of the following definitions.

_____ (a) any negatively charged ion

_____ (b) a systematic procedure for the separation and identification of anions, or other substances present in a sample

_____ (c) a solution of a substance dissolved in water

_____ (d) an insoluble solid substance produced from a reaction in aqueous solution

_____ (e) an instrument that spins test tubes to separate a precipitate from solution

_____ (f) the solution above a precipitate after insoluble particles are centrifuged from solution

_____ (g) the process of pouring a liquid from one container into another

     Key Terms: anion, aqueous solution, centrifuge, decant, precipitate (ppt), qualitative analysis, supernate

2. Which three anions are investigated in this experiment? (Refer to **Figure 1**.)

3. What color is the spot on blue litmus paper when testing an acidic solution? (Refer to **Figure 2**.)

4. Refer to the **Data Table** to answer the following.

    (a) Which anion is confirmed in test tube #1 by a *yellow* precipitate?   _____

    (b) Which anion is confirmed in test tube #2 by a *white* precipitate?   _____

    (c) Which anion is confirmed in test tube #3 by a *white* precipitate?   _____

5. Why is it necessary to use distilled water throughout the experiment?

---

* Answers at the end of the experiment.

6. Refer to the **Data Table** to determine which anions (I^-, Cl^-, $SO_4{}^{2-}$) are present and absent in an unknown solution given the following observations.

- The unknown solution in test tube #1 plus $AgNO_3$ gives a yellow precipitate.
- The supernate in test tube #1 is poured into test tube #3.
- The yellow precipitate in test tube #1 partially dissolves in NH_4OH.
- The supernate in test tube #1 is poured into test tube #2.
- The solution in test tube #2 is made acidic with HNO_3 and gives a white precipitate.
- The solution in test tube #3 plus $Ba(NO_3)_2$ gives a white precipitate.

Anion(s) **present** _____   Anion(s) **absent** _____

7. Refer to the **Data Table** to determine which anions (I^-, Cl^-, $SO_4{}^{2-}$) are present and absent in an unknown solution given the following observations.

- The unknown solution in test tube #1 plus $AgNO_3$ gives no reaction.
- The solution in test tube #1 is poured into test tube #3.
- The solution in test tube #3 plus $Ba(NO_3)_2$ gives a white precipitate.

Anion(s) **present** _____   Anion(s) **absent** _____

8. What safety precautions should be taken while performing this experiment?

EXPERIMENT

NAME _____

DATE _____

SECTION _____

DATA TABLE

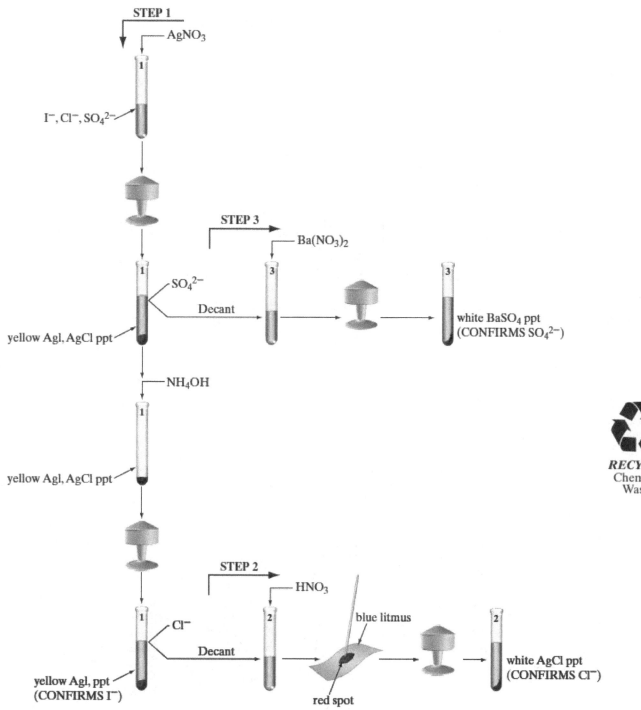

STEP 1

AgNO$_3$

I$^-$, Cl$^-$, SO$_4^{2-}$

STEP 3

Ba(NO$_3$)$_2$

SO$_4^{2-}$

Decant

white BaSO$_4$ ppt
(CONFIRMS SO$_4^{2-}$)

yellow AgI, AgCl ppt

NH$_4$OH

yellow AgI, AgCl ppt

STEP 2

HNO$_3$

blue litmus

Cl$^-$

Decant

red spot

white AgCl ppt
(CONFIRMS Cl$^-$)

yellow AgI, ppt
(CONFIRMS I$^-$)

RECYCLE
Chemical
Waste

B. Analysis of an Unknown Anion Solution   **UNKNOWN #** _____

Anion(s) **present** _____   Anion(s) **absent** _____

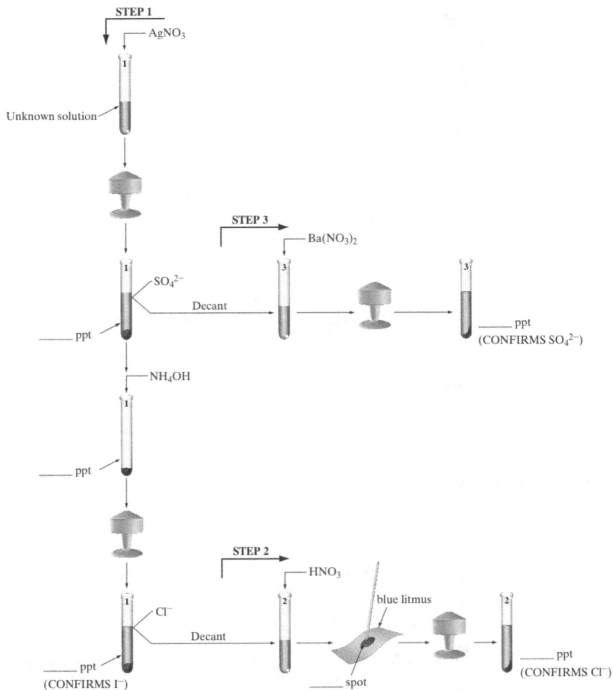

RECYCLE
Chemical
Waste

EXPERIMENT   NAME _____

DATE _____   SECTION _____

POSTLABORATORY ASSIGNMENT

1. Which anions are present and absent in an unknown solution given the following observations?

 • The unknown solution in test tube #1 plus $AgNO_3$ gives a yellow precipitate.
 • The supernate in test tube #1 is poured into test tube #3.
 • The yellow precipitate in test tube #1 partially dissolves in NH_4OH.
 • The supernate in test tube #1 is poured into test tube #2.
 • The solution in test tube #2 is made acidic with HNO_3 and gives a white precipitate.
 • The solution in test tube #3 plus $Ba(NO_3)_2$ gives no reaction.

  Anion(s) **present** _____   Anion(s) **absent** _____

2. Which anions are present and absent in an unknown solution given the following observations?

 • The unknown solution in test tube #1 plus $AgNO_3$ gives a white precipitate.
 • The supernate in test tube #1 is poured into test tube #3.
 • The white precipitate in test tube #1 dissolves completely in NH_4OH.
 • The solution in test tube #1 is poured into test tube #2.
 • The solution in test tube #2 is made acidic with HNO_3 and gives a white precipitate.
 • The solution in test tube #3 plus $Ba(NO_3)_2$ gives a white precipitate.

  Anion(s) **present** _____   Anion(s) **absent** _____

3. Provide the formula for the following monoatomic anions.

 (a) fluoride ion _____   (b) bromide ion _____

 (c) oxide ion   _____   (d) sulfide ion _____

 (e) nitride ion _____   (f) phosphide ion _____

4. Provide the formula for the following polyatomic anions.

 (a) nitrate ion _____   (b) nitrite ion _____

 (c) sulfate ion _____   (d) sulfite ion _____

 (e) chlorate ion _____   (f) chlorite ion _____

5. Complete the table below as shown by the example. Combine the ions into a correct formula, and name the compound.

	I^-	Cl^-	SO_4^{2-}
NH_4^+	NH_4I *ammonium iodide*		
Cd^{2+}			
Al^{3+}			

6. (optional) Complete the table below as shown by the example. Combine the ions into a correct formula, and name the compound.

	acetate ion	carbonate ion	phosphate ion
copper(II) ion	$Cu(C_2H_3O_2)_2$ *copper(II) acetate*		
cobalt(III) ion			
tin(IV) ion			

ANSWERS TO PRELABORATORY ASSIGNMENTS

1. See the Glossary.
2. I^-, Cl^-, SO_4^{2-}
3. A red spot indicates an acidic solution. If the spot is blue, add a few more drops of HNO_3.
4. (a) I^-; (b) Cl^-; and (c) SO_4^{2-}
5. Tap water contains ions that can interfere with the analysis.
6. All three anions (I^-, Cl^-, SO_4^{2-}) are present.
7. SO_4^{2-} is present; I^- and Cl^- are absent.
8. • Wear safety goggles; avoid contact with HNO_3, NH_4OH, and $AgNO_3$. If contacted, wash the area immediately with water.
   • Dispose of chemical waste in the designated container.

EXPERIMENT

Molecular Models and Chemical Bonds

OBJECTIVES

- To construct models of molecules with single, double, and triple bonds.
- To draw the structural formula for a molecule based on the molecular model.
- To draw the electron dot formula corresponding to the structural formula.
- To draw the structural and electron dot formulas for unknown molecular models.

DISCUSSION

The attraction between two atoms in a molecule is called a chemical bond. In a **covalent bond**, two nonmetal atoms are attracted to each other by sharing valence electrons. The **valence electrons** are the electrons farthest from the nucleus in the outermost portion of an atom. The number of valence electrons can be found by referring to the periodic table. The group number of an element indicates the number of valence electrons. For example, fluorine is in Group VIIA/17 and has seven valence electrons (7 e−).

Example Exercise 1 • Valence Electrons and the Periodic Table

Refer to the group number in the periodic table and determine the valence electrons for the following elements: (a) H; (b) C; (c) O; and (d) Cl.

Solution: (a) Hydrogen is in group IA/1; thus, H has **one** valence electron.
   (b) Carbon is in Group IVA/14; thus, C has **four** valence electrons.
   (c) Oxygen is in Group VIA/16; thus, O has **six** valence electrons.
   (d) Chlorine is in Group VIIA/17; thus, Cl has **seven** valence electrons.

From Experiment 18 of *Laboratory Manual to Accompany Introductory Chemistry: Concepts and Critical Thinking*, Sixth Edition.
Charles H. Corwin. Copyright © 2013 by Pearson Education, Inc. All rights reserved.

In this experiment, we will draw the **structural formula** and **electron dot formula** for molecules after building a model. A model is constructed from spherical balls and connectors, where each ball represents an atom and each connector a single bond. Since a **single bond** shares two electrons, each connector represents an electron pair.

A **double bond** shares two pairs of electrons. A molecular model is constructed using two connectors to represent the double bond. A **triple bond** shares three pairs of electrons. A molecular model is constructed using three connectors to represent the triple bond.

The following example exercises illustrate the structural formula and electron dot formula for molecular models having single, double, and triple bonds.

Example Exercise 2 • Structural and Electron Dot Formula for CHCl₃

The molecular model of chloroform is sketched below. Draw (a) the structural formula and (b) the electron dot formula. Each atom (excluding H) should be surrounded by an octet of electrons. (c) Verify the electron dot formula by checking the total number of electron dots against the sum of all valence electrons.

chloroform, CHCl₃

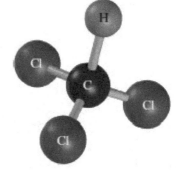

Solution: (a) Each stick represents a single bond, so the structural formula is

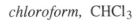

$$
\begin{array}{c}
\text{H} \\
| \\
\text{Cl} - \text{C} - \text{Cl} \\
| \\
\text{Cl}
\end{array}
$$

(b) Each dash in the structural formula indicates an electron pair; therefore,

$$
\begin{array}{c}
\text{H} \\
\text{Cl} \; \overset{\bullet\bullet}{\underset{\bullet\bullet}{\text{C}}} \; \text{Cl} \\
\text{Cl}
\end{array}
$$

Hydrogen and carbon are complete as shown; two electrons and eight electrons, respectively. However, each chlorine also requires an octet, which we will complete as follows:

$$
\begin{array}{c}
\text{H} \\
:\!\overset{\bullet\bullet}{\underset{\bullet\bullet}{\text{Cl}}}\!:\overset{\bullet\bullet}{\underset{\bullet\bullet}{\text{C}}}:\overset{\bullet\bullet}{\underset{\bullet\bullet}{\text{Cl}}}\!: \\
:\!\overset{\bullet\bullet}{\underset{\bullet\bullet}{\text{Cl}}}\!:
\end{array}
$$

(c) To verify the above electron dot formula, we will find the sum of all valence electrons.

$$
\begin{aligned}
1\ H\ (1 \times 1\ e-) &= 1\ e- \\
1\ C\ (1 \times 4\ e-) &= 4\ e- \\
3\ Cl\ (3 \times 7\ e-) &= \underline{21\ e-} \\
\textit{sum of valence electrons} &= 26\ e-
\end{aligned}
$$

There are 26 valence electrons, and 26 dots were used in the electron dot formula; thus, the formula is verified.

Example Exercise 3 • Structural and Electron Dot Formula for H_2CO

A molecular model of formaldehyde is sketched below. Draw the (a) structural formula and (b) electron dot formula. (c) Find the sum of all valence electrons to verify the electron dot formula.

formaldehyde, H_2CO

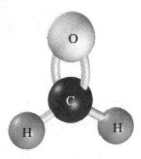

Solution: (a) Two connectors joining the carbon and oxygen atoms represent a double bond. The structural formula can be shown as

$$
\begin{array}{c}
O \\
\| \\
H - C - H
\end{array}
$$

(b) Each single bond contains one electron pair, and the double bond two electron pairs.

$$
\begin{array}{c}
O \\
:: \\
H : C : H
\end{array}
$$

Hydrogen shares two electrons and is stable. Carbon shares a total of eight electrons and satisfies the **octet rule**. Oxygen has only four of the eight electrons necessary to complete the octet. Therefore, we will add two unshared electron pairs.

$$
\begin{array}{c}
: \ddot{O} \\
:: \\
H : C : H
\end{array}
$$

(c) We can verify the above electron dot formula as follows:

$$
\begin{array}{lcl}
2\,\text{H}\,(2 \times 1\,\text{e}-) & = & 2\,\text{e}- \\
1\,\text{C}\,(1 \times 4\,\text{e}-) & = & 4\,\text{e}- \\
1\,\text{O}\,(1 \times 6\,\text{e}-) & = & \underline{6\,\text{e}-} \\
\textit{sum of valence electrons} & = & 12\,\text{e}-
\end{array}
$$

The 12 valence electrons equal the 12 electron dots and verify the formula.

Example Exercise 4 • Structural and Electron Dot Formula for HCN

A molecular model of hydrogen cyanide is sketched below. Draw (a) the structural formula and (b) the electron dot formula. (c) Verify the electron dot formula.

hydrogen cyanide, HCN

Solution: (a) The three connectors linking the carbon and nitrogen represent a triple pair of electrons.

$$\text{H} - \text{C} \equiv \text{N}$$

(b) We can draw an electron dot formula after realizing the triple bond contains three electron pairs.

$$\text{H} : \text{C} ::: \text{N}$$

In the above formula, nitrogen shares only six electrons. Therefore, we must add one unshared electron pair.

$$\text{H} : \text{C} ::: \text{N} :$$

(c) Let's verify the preceding electron dot formula.

$$
\begin{array}{lcl}
1\,\text{H}\,(1 \times 1\,\text{e}-) & = & 1\,\text{e}- \\
1\,\text{C}\,(1 \times 4\,\text{e}-) & = & 4\,\text{e}- \\
1\,\text{N}\,(1 \times 5\,\text{e}-) & = & \underline{5\,\text{e}-} \\
\textit{sum of valence electrons} & = & 10\,\text{e}-
\end{array}
$$

The 10 valence electrons verify the 10 e– dots.

EQUIPMENT and CHEMICALS

- Molecular Model Kit
  Student molecular model sets (ISBN: 0-205-08136-3) are available
  from Prentice Hall @ 1-800-922-0579 (www.prenhall.com).

Directions for Building Molecular Models

When constructing a molecular model, a hole in a ball represents a missing electron that is necessary to satisfy the octet rule. If two balls are joined by a rigid connector, the connector represents a single bond. If two balls are joined by two flexible connectors, the two connectors represent a double bond. If two balls are joined by three flexible connectors, the three connectors represent a triple bond.

one rigid connector	—	single bond (one e– pair)
two flexible connectors	—	double bond (two e– pairs)
three flexible connectors	—	triple bond (three e– pairs)

A molecular model uses different color balls to represent hydrogen, carbon, oxygen, chlorine, bromine, iodine, and nitrogen atoms. The color code for each ball is as follows:

white ball	—	hydrogen atom (one hole)
black ball	—	carbon atom (four holes)
red ball	—	oxygen atom (two holes)
green ball	—	chlorine atom (one hole)
orange ball	—	bromine atom (one hole)
purple ball	—	iodine atom (one hole)
blue ball	—	nitrogen atom (three holes)

Note: For some compounds, it may be difficult to determine the central atom. In this experiment the central atom is shown in **bold** to help build the molecular model; e.g., $H_2\mathbf{O}$.

PROCEDURE

1. Construct molecular models for each compound on the following page. Sketch the model in the Data Table.

2. Draw the structural formula corresponding to the molecular model.

3. Draw the electron dot formula corresponding to the structural formula. Complete the octet by surrounding each atom with 8 electrons (2 electrons for a hydrogen atom).

4. Verify each electron dot formula by summing the valence electrons for the molecule, using the periodic table. This sum should equal the total number of dots in the electron dot formula.

A. Molecular Models with Single Bonds

(a) $\mathbf{H}_2$ (b) $\mathbf{Cl}_2$

(c) $\mathbf{Br}_2$ (d) $\mathbf{I}_2$

(e) H**Cl** (f) H**Br**

(g) I**Cl** (h) **C**H_4

(i) **C**H_2Cl_2 (j) H**O**Cl

(k) $H_2\mathbf{O}_2$ (l) **N**H_3

(m) $\mathbf{N}_2H_4$ (n) **N**H_2**O**H

Note: The central atom is shown in **bold**.

B. Molecular Models with Double Bonds

(a) $\mathbf{O}_2$ (b) $\mathbf{C}_2H_4$

(c) H**ON**O (d) H**CO**OH

(e) $\mathbf{C}_2H_3Cl$

C. Molecular Models with Triple Bonds

(a) $\mathbf{N}_2$ (b) $\mathbf{C}_2H_2$

(c) H**OC**N

D. Molecular Models with Two Double Bonds

(a) **C**O_2 (b) $\mathbf{C}_3H_4$

E. Unknown Molecular Models

The Instructor will provide models of unknown molecules. Draw the structural formula for each unknown model and the electron dot formula corresponding to each structural formula.

EXPERIMENT   NAME   _____

DATE   _____   SECTION   _____

PRELABORATORY ASSIGNMENT*

1. Provide the key term that corresponds to each of the following definitions.

_____ (a) the statement that an atom tends to bond in such a way so as to acquire eight electrons in its outer shell

_____ (b) the electrons in the outermost *s* and *p* sublevels of an atom that form chemical bonds

_____ (c) a bond characterized by the sharing of one or more pairs of valence electrons

_____ (d) a bond composed of one electron pair shared between two atoms

_____ (e) a bond composed of two electron pairs shared between two atoms

_____ (f) a bond composed of three electron pairs shared between two atoms

_____ (g) a diagram of a molecule in which each atom is represented by its symbol surrounded by two dots for each pair of bonding or nonbonding electrons

_____ (h) a diagram of a molecule that shows the chemical symbol of each atom and a dash representing each pair of bonding electrons

    Key Terms: covalent bond, double bond, electron dot formula, octet rule, single bond, structural formula, triple bond, valence electrons

2. Refer to the periodic table and predict the number of valence electrons for atoms of the following elements:

  (a)   carbon   (b)   hydrogen

  (c)   oxygen   (d)   nitrogen

  (e)   chlorine   (f)   bromine

3. What do each of the following represent in the molecular model kit?

  (a)   one rigid connector   (b)   two flexible connectors

  (c)   three flexible connectors   (d)   white ball

  (e)   black ball   (f)   red ball

  (g)   green ball   (h)   orange ball

  (i)   purple ball   (j)   blue ball

_____

* *Answers at the end of the experiment.*

4. Draw the structural formula corresponding to each of the following molecular models.

(a)

(b)

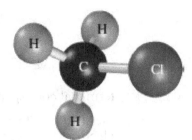

(c)

5. Draw the electron dot formula corresponding to the structural formula of the above models.

(a)   (b)

(c)

6. Verify the electron dot formula and sum the valence electrons for the above models.

(a) **IBr**   *Total Valence Electrons* ___

(b) **CH₃Cl**   *Total Valence Electrons* ___

(c) **Cl₂CO**   *Total Valence Electrons* ___

EXPERIMENT NAME _____

DATE _____ SECTION _____

DATA TABLE

A. Molecular Models with Single Bonds **Model Kit #_____**

Molecule	Molecular Model	Structural Formula	Electron Dot Formula	Valence Electrons
(a) H_2				
(b) Cl_2				
(c) Br_2				
(d) I_2				

Molecule	Molecular Model	Structural Formula	Electron Dot Formula	Valence Electrons
(e) HCl				
(f) HBr				
(g) ICl				
(h) CH$_4$				
(i) CH$_2$Cl$_2$				

Molecule	Molecular Model	Structural Formula	Electron Dot Formula	Valence Electrons
(j) HOCl				
(k) H_2O_2				
(l) NH_3				
(m) N_2H_4				
(n) NH_2OH				

B. Molecular Models with Double Bonds

Molecule	Molecular Model	Structural Formula	Electron Dot Formula	Valence Electrons
(a) O_2				
(b) C_2H_4				
(c) HONO				
(d) HCOOH				
(e) C_2H_3Cl				

C. Molecular Models with Triple Bonds

Molecule	Molecular Model	Structural Formula	Electron Dot Formula	Valence Electrons
(a) N_2				
(b) C_2H_2				
(c) HOCN				

D. Molecular Models with Two Double Bonds

(a) CO_2				
(b) C_3H_4				

E. Unknown Molecular Models

Molecule	Molecular Model	Structural Formula	Electron Dot Formula	Valence Electrons
#1				
#2				
#3				
#4				
#5				

EXPERIMENT   NAME _____

DATE _____   SECTION _____

POSTLABORATORY ASSIGNMENT

1. Find the number of valence electrons (VE) for the following molecules. Draw the electron dot formula and structural formula for each molecule. The central atom is shown in **bold.**

Molecule	Electron Dot Formula	Structural Formula
(a) **H**OBr VE =		
(b) **P**I$_3$ VE =		
(c) **Si**F$_4$ VE =		
(d) **C**S$_2$ VE =		
(e) **S**O$_2$ VE =		

2. Refer to the electron dot formula for each molecule in the preceding question. Using VSEPR theory, predict the electron pair geometry and molecular shape for each molecule.

Molecule	Electron Pair Geometry	Molecular Shape
(a) HOBr		
(b) PI_3		
(c) SiF_4		
(d) CS_2		
(e) SO_2		

3. (optional) A hydrogen ion bonds to an ammonia molecule, NH_3, forming the ammonium ion. Draw the electron dot and structural formulas for NH_4^+. Label the coordinate covalent bond.

ANSWERS TO PRELABORATORY ASSIGNMENTS

1. See the Glossary.
2. The number of valence electrons corresponds to the group number of the element in the periodic table; thus,
   - (a) C = 4 (Group IVA/14)
   - (b) H = 1 (Group IA/1)
   - (c) O = 6 (Group VIA/16)
   - (d) N = 5 (Group VA/15)
   - (e) Cl = 7 (Group VIIA/17)
   - (f) Br = 7 (Group VIIA/17)
3. (a) single bond (one e– pair)
   - (b) double bond (two e– pairs)
   - (c) triple bond (three e– pairs)
   - (d) hydrogen atom
   - (e) carbon atom
   - (f) oxygen atom
   - (g) chlorine atom
   - (h) bromine atom
   - (i) iodine atom
   - (j) nitrogen atom

4. (a)   I—Br

(b)

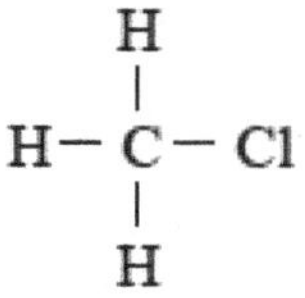

$$
\begin{array}{c}
\text{H} \\
| \\
\text{H}-\text{C}-\text{Cl} \\
| \\
\text{H}
\end{array}
$$

(c)

$$
\begin{array}{c}
\text{O} \\
\parallel \\
\text{Cl}-\text{C}-\text{Cl}
\end{array}
$$

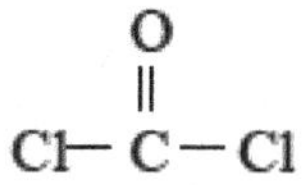

5. (a) $:\overset{\cdot\cdot}{\text{I}}:\overset{\cdot\cdot}{\underset{\cdot\cdot}{\text{Br}}}:$

(b)

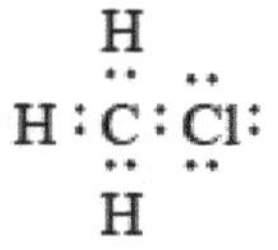

$$
\begin{array}{c}
\text{H} \\
\text{H}:\text{C}:\overset{\cdot\cdot}{\underset{\cdot\cdot}{\text{Cl}}}: \\
\text{H}
\end{array}
$$

(c)

$$
\begin{array}{c}
:\text{O}: \\
\overset{\cdot\cdot}{\underset{\cdot\cdot}{\text{Cl}}}:\text{C}:\overset{\cdot\cdot}{\underset{\cdot\cdot}{\text{Cl}}}:
\end{array}
$$

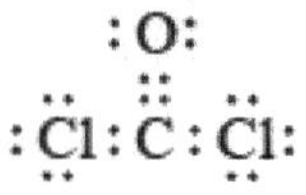

6. (a) 14 e–; (b) 14 e–; (c) 24 e–

Analysis of a Penny

OBJECTIVES

- To state observations that are evidence for a chemical reaction.
- To write chemical equations from the descriptions of reactions.
- To determine the percentages of copper and zinc in a "zinc penny."
- To gain experience in observing chemical reactions.

DISCUSSION

Most ordinary chemical reactions can be classified as one of five basic types. The first type of reaction occurs when two or more **reactants** combine to form a single **product**. This type of reaction is called a *combination reaction*.

$$A + Z \rightarrow AZ$$

A second type of reaction occurs when a single compound breaks down into two or more simpler substances, often with the use of a **catalyst** to speed up the reaction. This type is called a *decomposition reaction*.

$$AZ \rightarrow A + Z$$

From Experiment 10 of *Laboratory Manual to Accompany Introductory Chemistry: Concepts and Critical Thinking*, Sixth Edition. Charles H. Corwin. Copyright © 2013 by Pearson Education, Inc. All rights reserved.

A third type of reaction occurs when one element displaces another. For this to occur, a more active element that is higher in the **activity series** displaces an element that is lower in the series. This type is called a *single-replacement reaction.*

$$A + BZ \rightarrow AZ + B$$

A fourth type of reaction occurs when two substances in **aqueous solution** switch partners; that is, an anion of one substance exchanges with another. Usually one of the products is an insoluble substance called a **precipitate**. This type is called a *double-replacement reaction.*

$$AX + BZ \rightarrow AZ + BX$$

A fifth type of reaction occurs when an acid and a base react to form a salt and water. This is a special type of double-replacement reaction, and is called a *neutralization reaction.*

$$HX + BOH \rightarrow BX + HOH$$

Notice that the hydrogen ion in the acid neutralizes the hydroxide ion in the base to form water. If water is written as HOH, the neutralization is obvious and the equation may be easier to balance.

In this experiment, you will observe evidence for a chemical reaction. Evidence for a reaction includes: (1) a *gas is released*; (2) a *precipitate is produced*; (3) a *permanent color change* is observed; (4) an *energy change* is noted, such as heat or light being given off.

In order to describe a chemical reaction, chemists use shorthand symbols when writing a chemical equation. Table 1 lists some of these symbols.

Table 1 Chemical Equation Symbols

Symbol	Explanation of Symbol
$\rightarrow$	produces, yields *(separates the reactants from the products)*
+	reacts with, added to *(separates two or more reactants or products)*
$\xrightarrow{\Delta}$	heat is a catalyst for the reaction
$\xrightarrow{Fe}$	iron is a catalyst for the reaction
NR	no reaction
(g)	gaseous substance
(l)	liquid substance
(s)	solid substance or precipitate
(aq)	aqueous solution

To write a chemical equation it is necessary to predict the products from a reaction. To aid you in writing equations, the products are given for each reaction in this experiment. You only need to convert the given reactions into chemical equations and balance the reactants and products. The following examples illustrate.

Combination Reaction

calcium(s) + oxygen(g) $\rightarrow$ calcium oxide(s)

$$2\ Ca(s)\ +\ O_2(g)\ \rightarrow\ 2\ CaO(s)$$

Decomposition Reaction

lithium hydrogen carbonate(s) $\overset{\Delta}{\rightarrow}$ lithium carbonate(s) + water(g) + carbon dioxide(g)

$$2\ LiHCO_3(s)\ \overset{\Delta}{\rightarrow}\ Li_2CO_3(s)\ +\ H_2O(g)\ +\ CO_2(g)$$

Single-Replacement Reaction

zinc(s) + hydrochloric acid(aq) $\rightarrow$ zinc chloride(aq) + hydrogen(g)

$$Zn(s)\ +\ 2\ HCl(aq)\ \rightarrow\ ZnCl_2(aq)\ +\ H_2(g)$$

Double-Replacement Reaction

potassium carbonate(aq) + calcium chloride(aq) $\rightarrow$ calcium carbonate(s) + potassium chloride(aq)

$$K_2CO_3(aq)\ +\ CaCl_2(aq)\ \rightarrow\ CaCO_3(s)\ +\ 2\ KCl(aq)$$

Neutralization Reaction

nitric acid(aq) + barium hydroxide(aq) $\rightarrow$ barium nitrate(aq) + water

$$2\ HNO_3(aq)\ +\ Ba(OH)_2(aq)\ \rightarrow\ Ba(NO_3)_2(aq)\ +\ 2\ HOH(l)$$

Analysis of a "Zinc Penny"

In 1982 the *U.S. Mint* stopped making copper pennies because they cost more than 1¢ to mint. The *U.S. Mint* started making pennies from zinc "blanks" plated with a thin layer of copper metal. Although copper and zinc pennies look similar, a "zinc penny" weighs about 20% less.

In this experiment you will cut a "zinc penny" to expose the zinc metal and drop the penny into sulfuric acid. Copper does not react with acid, but zinc does react and leaves a thin copper shell. The chemical equations for the two metals and sulfuric acid are:

$$Cu(s)\ +\ H_2SO_4(aq)\ \rightarrow\ NR$$
$$Zn(s)\ +\ H_2SO_4(aq)\ \rightarrow\ ZnSO_4(aq)\ +\ H_2(g)$$

The following example exercise illustrates the calculation for the percentages of copper and zinc in a "zinc penny."

Example Exercise 1 • Percent Composition of a "Zinc Penny"

A 1995 penny having a mass of 2.536 g is cut as shown in Figure 1 and dropped into sulfuric acid. After the zinc has reacted, the copper shell is found to have a mass of 0.063 g. Calculate the percentages of copper and zinc in the "zinc penny."

Solution: The percentage of copper is simply the ratio of the mass of Cu metal to the mass of the penny; that is,

$$\frac{0.063 \text{ g}}{2.536 \text{ g}} \times 100\% = 2.5\% \text{ Cu}$$

The percentage of zinc is the ratio of the mass of Zn metal to the mass of the original penny. The mass of Zn corresponds to the mass loss of the penny: 2.536 g − 0.063 g = 2.473 g. Thus,

$$\frac{2.473 \text{ g}}{2.536 \text{ g}} \times 100\% = 97.52\% \text{ Zn}$$

Experimentally, the 1995 "zinc penny" is 2.5% Cu and 97.52% zinc.

Students often ask if it is illegal to destroy a penny. According to a U.S. Treasury official: *"the law provides criminal penalties for anyone who **fraudulently** alters, defaces, mutilates, impairs, diminishes, falsifies, scales or lightens any of the coins coined at the mints of the United States."* Since we are not intending to defraud, this experiment is **legal**.

EQUIPMENT and CHEMICALS

A. Instructor Demonstrations

- crucible tongs
- deflagrating spoon
- magnesium, Mg ribbon
- sulfur, S powder

B–F. Student Experiments

- ring stand & ring
- 13 x 100 mm test tubes (6) & test tube rack
- test tube holder
- test tube brush
- wash bottle with distilled water
- 250-mL Erlenmeyer flask
- 100-mL beaker
- copper(II) sulfate pentahydrate, solid $CuSO_4 \cdot 5H_2O$
- sodium hydrogen carbonate, solid $NaHCO_3$
- wooden splints
- copper, Cu wire
- magnesium, Mg turnings

- calcium, Ca turnings
- hydrochloric acid, 0.1 M HCl
- silver nitrate, 0.1 M $AgNO_3$
- copper(II) nitrate, 0.1 M $Cu(NO_3)_2$
- aluminum nitrate, 0.1 M $Al(NO_3)_3$
- potassium carbonate, 0.5 M K_2CO_3
- sodium phosphate, 0.5 M Na_3PO_4
- nitric acid, 0.1 M HNO_3
- sulfuric acid, 0.1 M H_2SO_4
- phosphoric acid, 0.1 M H_3PO_4
- sodium hydroxide, 0.5 M NaOH
- phenolphthalein indicator
- "zinc penny" (post-1982 mint date)
- dilute sulfuric acid, 3 M H_2SO_4
- acetone, C_3H_6O

PROCEDURE

General Directions: For Procedures A–E, record your observations in the Data Table. Since a "zinc penny" requires hours to react completely, it is advisable to start with Procedure F, and then continue with Procedures A–E.

A. Instructor Demonstration – Combination Reactions

1. Hold a 2-cm strip of magnesium ribbon with crucible tongs, and ignite the metal in a hot burner flame.

2. Put about 1 g of sulfur in a deflagrating spoon. Dim the lights and ignite the powder with a hot burner flame. Place the burning sulfur under a fume hood to avoid the strong odor of sulfur dioxide gas.

RECYCLE
Chemical
Waste

B. Decomposition Reactions

1. Put a pea-sized portion of copper(II) sulfate pentahydrate crystals into a dry test tube. Grasp the test tube with a test tube holder and heat with a burner (see Figure 1.1). Note the color change, and observe the inside surface at the top of the test tube.

2. Add sodium hydrogen carbonate (baking soda) into a 250-mL Erlenmeyer flask so as to cover the bottom of the flask. Support the flask on a ring stand, using a wire gauze.
   (a) Hold a flaming splint in the mouth of the flask, and record how long it burns.
   (b) Heat the flask strongly with the laboratory burner until moisture is observed; hold a flaming splint in the mouth of the flask, and record how long it burns.

C. Single-Replacement Reactions

1. Put 20 drops of silver nitrate solution into a test tube, and add a small piece of copper wire. Allow a few minutes for reaction and then record your observation.

2. Put 20 drops of hydrochloric acid into a test tube, and add a small piece of magnesium metal. Record your observation.

3. Put 20 drops of distilled water into a test tube, and add a small piece of calcium metal. Record your observation.

D. Double-Replacement Reactions

1–3. Put 10 drops of silver nitrate, copper(II) nitrate, and aluminum nitrate solutions into separate test tubes #1–3. Add a few drops of potassium carbonate solution to test tubes #1, #2, and #3. Observe the reactions, and record your observations.

4–6. Put 10 drops of silver nitrate, copper(II) nitrate, and aluminum nitrate solutions into separate test tubes #4–6. Add a few drops of sodium phosphate solution to test tubes #4, #5, and #6. Observe the reactions, and record your observations.

E. Neutralization Reactions

1. Put 10 drops of nitric acid, sulfuric acid, and phosphoric acid into test tubes #1–3. Add one drop of indicator to each of the test tubes. Add sodium hydroxide dropwise into test tube #1 until a permanent color change is observed.

> **Note:** The indicator is colorless in acid, and pink in a basic solution.

RECYCLE
Chemical
Waste

2. Add drops of dilute sodium hydroxide solution to test tube #2 until a permanent color change is observed.

3. Add drops of dilute sodium hydroxide solution to test tube #3 until a permanent color change is observed.

F. Percentages of Copper and Zinc in a Penny

1. Obtain a post-1982 penny, and record the mint date. Using metal shears, cut the coin as shown in Figure 1.

Figure 1 Exposing Zinc in a Penny A "zinc penny" should be cut as shown to ensure a rapid and complete reaction with sulfuric acid.

2. Weigh the penny on a balance, and record the mass.

3. Drop the penny into a 100-mL beaker, and add about 20 mL of dilute sulfuric acid. The reaction requires about 3 hours for the zinc in the coin to react completely.

4. When the coin stops producing gas bubbles, discard the acid, and wash the coin with distilled water.

5. Rinse the coin with acetone, and discard the rinse solution. When the coin appears dry, weigh the copper shell and record the mass in the Data Table.

6. Calculate the percentages of copper and zinc in the penny.

EXPERIMENT   NAME _____

DATE _____   SECTION _____

PRELABORATORY ASSIGNMENT*

1. Provide the key term that corresponds to each of the following definitions.

_____ (a) a substance undergoing a chemical reaction

_____ (b) a substance resulting from a chemical reaction

_____ (c) a substance that speeds up a chemical reaction

_____ (d) a relative order of metals arranged according to their ability to undergo reaction

_____ (e) a solution of a substance dissolved in water

_____ (f) an insoluble solid substance produced from a reaction in aqueous solution

_____ (g) the solution above a precipitate after insoluble particles separate from solution

     Key Terms: aqueous solution, activity series, catalyst, precipitate (ppt), product, reactant, supernate

2. Classify the following types of chemical reactions.

     (a) $2\,Na(s)\ +\ Cl_2(g)$ $\rightarrow$ $2\,NaCl(s)$

     (b) $Na_2CO_3(s)$ $\overset{\Delta}{\rightarrow}$ $Na_2O(s)\ +\ CO_2(g)$

     (c) $2\,Na(s)\ +\ 2\,H_2O(aq)$ $\rightarrow$ $2\,NaOH(aq)\ +\ H_2\,(s)$

     (d) $AgNO_3(aq)\ +\ NaCl(aq)$ $\rightarrow$ $AgCl(s)\ +\ NaNO_3(aq)$

     (e) $HNO_3(aq)\ +\ KOH(aq)$ $\rightarrow$ $KNO_3(aq)\ +\ H_2O(l)$

3. State four observations that provide evidence for a chemical reaction.

     (a)

     (b)

     (c)

     (d)

_____

* Answers at the end of the experiment.

4. Supply the symbol for each of the following in a chemical equation.

    (a)   gas reactant or product

    (b)   liquid reactant or product

    (c)   solid reactant or product

    (d)   aqueous solution

    (e)   precipitate in solution

    (f)   heat as a catalyst

    (g)   no reaction

5. What color is phenolphthalein indicator:

    (a)   in an acidic solution?

    (b)   in a basic solution?

6. Based on the mint date, which of following pennies *cannot* be used in this experiment: 1980, 1990, or 2000?

7. A 2010 penny has a mass of 2.541 g and produces a copper shell with a mass of 0.064 g. Refer to Example Exercise 1 and find the (a) %Cu and (b) %Zn in the penny.

8. What safety precautions must be observed in this experiment?

EXPERIMENT   NAME _____

DATE _____   SECTION _____

DATA TABLE

Procedure	*Observation*

A. Instructor Demonstration – Combination Reactions

    1. $Mg + O_2 \xrightarrow{\Delta}$ _____

    2. $S + O_2 \xrightarrow{\Delta}$ _____

B. Decomposition Reactions

    1. $CuSO_4 \cdot 5H_2O \xrightarrow{\Delta}$ _____

    2. (a) $NaHCO_3$ _____

        (b) $NaHCO_3 \xrightarrow{\Delta}$ _____

C. Single-Replacement Reactions

    1. $Cu + AgNO_3 \rightarrow$ _____

    2. $Mg + HCl \rightarrow$ _____

    3. $Ca + H_2O \rightarrow$ _____

D. Double-Replacement Reactions

    1. $AgNO_3 + K_2CO_3 \rightarrow$ _____

    2. $Cu(NO_3)_2 + K_2CO_3 \rightarrow$ _____

    3. $Al(NO_3)_3 + K_2CO_3 \rightarrow$ _____

    4. $AgNO_3 + Na_3PO_4 \rightarrow$ _____

    5. $Cu(NO_3)_2 + Na_3PO_4 \rightarrow$ _____

    6. $Al(NO_3)_3 + Na_3PO_4 \rightarrow$ _____

E. Neutralization Reactions

    1. $HNO_3 + NaOH \rightarrow$ _____

    2. $H_2SO_4 + NaOH \rightarrow$ _____

    3. $H_3PO_4 + NaOH \rightarrow$ _____

RECYCLE
Chemical
Waste

Converting Word Equations into Balanced Chemical Equations

A. Instructor Demonstration – Combination Reactions

1. magnesium(s) + oxygen(g) $\xrightarrow{\Delta}$ magnesium oxide(s)

   Mg(s) + O_2(g) $\xrightarrow{\Delta}$

2. sulfur(s) + oxygen(g) $\xrightarrow{\Delta}$ sulfur dioxide(g)

   S(s) + O_2(g) $\xrightarrow{\Delta}$

B. Decomposition Reactions

1. copper(II) sulfate pentahydrate(s) $\xrightarrow{\Delta}$ copper(II) sulfate(s) + water(g)

   $CuSO_4 \cdot 5H_2O$(s) $\xrightarrow{\Delta}$

2. sodium hydrogen carbonate(s) $\xrightarrow{\Delta}$ sodium carbonate(s) + water(g) + carbon dioxide(g)

   $NaHCO_3$(s) $\xrightarrow{\Delta}$

C. Single-Replacement Reactions

1. copper(s) + silver nitrate(aq) $\rightarrow$ copper(II) nitrate(aq) + silver(s)

   Cu(s) + $AgNO_3$(aq) $\rightarrow$

2. magnesium(s) + hydrochloric acid(aq) $\rightarrow$ magnesium chloride(aq) + hydrogen(g)

   Mg(s) + HCl(aq) $\rightarrow$

3. calcium(s) + water(l) $\rightarrow$ calcium hydroxide(s) + hydrogen(g)

   Ca(s) + H_2O(l) $\rightarrow$

D. Double-Replacement Reactions

1. silver nitrate(aq) + potassium carbonate(aq) $\rightarrow$ silver carbonate(s) + potassium nitrate(aq)

    $AgNO_3(aq)$ + $K_2CO_3(aq)$ $\rightarrow$

2. copper(II) nitrate(aq) + potassium carbonate(aq) $\rightarrow$ copper(II) carbonate(s) + potassium nitrate(aq)

    $Cu(NO_3)_2(aq)$ + $K_2CO_3(aq)$ $\rightarrow$

3. aluminum nitrate(aq)+potassium carbonate(aq) $\rightarrow$ aluminum carbonate(s)+potassium nitrate(aq)

    $Al(NO_3)_3(aq)$ + $K_2CO_3(aq)$ $\rightarrow$

4. silver nitrate(aq) + sodium phosphate(aq) $\rightarrow$ silver phosphate(s) + sodium nitrate(aq)

    $AgNO_3(aq)$ + $Na_3PO_4(aq)$ $\rightarrow$

5. copper(II) nitrate(aq) + sodium phosphate(aq) $\rightarrow$ copper(II) phosphate(s) + sodium nitrate(aq)

    $Cu(NO_3)_2(aq)$ + $Na_3PO_4(aq)$ $\rightarrow$

6. aluminum nitrate(aq) + sodium phosphate(aq) $\rightarrow$ aluminum phosphate(s) + sodium nitrate(aq)

    $Al(NO_3)_3(aq)$ + $Na_3PO_4(aq)$ $\rightarrow$

E. Neutralization Reactions

1. nitric acid(aq)   +   sodium hydroxide(aq) $\rightarrow$ sodium nitrate(aq)   +   water(l)

    $HNO_3(aq)$ + $NaOH(aq)$ $\rightarrow$

2. sulfuric acid(aq)   +   sodium hydroxide(aq) $\rightarrow$ sodium sulfate(aq)   +   water(l)

    $H_2SO_4(aq)$ + $NaOH(aq)$ $\rightarrow$

3. phosphoric acid(aq) + sodium hydroxide(aq) $\rightarrow$ sodium phosphate(aq)   +   water(l)

    $H_3PO_4(aq)$ + $NaOH(aq)$ $\rightarrow$

F. Percentages of Copper and Zinc in a Penny   **Mint Date** _____

       mass of "zinc penny"   _____ g

       mass of copper   _____ g

       mass of zinc   _____ g

Show the calculation for the percentage copper in the penny (see Example Exercise 1).

RECYCLE
Chemical
Waste

       Percentage copper   _____ % Cu

Show the calculation for the percentage zinc in the penny.

       Percentage zinc   _____ % Zn

EXPERIMENT   NAME   _____

DATE   _____   SECTION   _____

POSTLABORATORY ASSIGNMENT

1. Provide the chemical formula for the substance described in each of the chemical reactions.

    (a)   the white smoke produced from reaction **A.1**   _____

    (b)   the strong odor produced from reaction **A.2**   _____

    (c)   the colorless gas produced from reaction **B.1**   _____

    (d)   the flame-extinguishing gas from reaction **B.2**   _____

    (e)   the gray solid produced from reaction **C.1**   _____

    (f)   the colorless gas produced from reaction **C.2**   _____

    (g)   the white ppt produced from reaction **C.3**   _____

    (h)   the cream ppt produced from reaction **D.1**   _____

    (i)   the blue-white ppt produced from reaction **D.2**   _____

    (j)   the white ppt produced from reaction **D.3**   _____

    (k)   the yellow ppt produced from reaction **D.4**   _____

    (l)   the blue-white ppt produced from reaction **D.5**   _____

    (m)   the white ppt produced from reaction **D.6**   _____

    (n)   the acid reacting in reaction **E.1**   _____

    (o)   the acid reacting in reaction **E.2**   _____

    (p)   the acid reacting in reaction **E.3**   _____

    (q)   the base reacting in reactions **E.1– E.3**   _____

2. Indicate reaction (*Rxn*) or no reaction (*NR*) when a small piece of tin metal is dropped into the following aqueous solutions.

    (a) $Ca(NO_3)_2$(aq)   _____   (b) $Cr(NO_3)_3$(aq)   _____

    (c) $Ni(NO_3)_2$(aq)   _____   (d) $Pb(NO_3)_2$(aq)   _____

    (e) HNO_3(aq)   _____   (f) $AgNO_3$(aq)   _____

3. Indicate whether the following compounds are soluble (*sol*) or insoluble (*insol*) in water.

(a) NH_4Cl _____   (b) $Fe(C_2H_3O_2)_3$ _____

(c) $Mg(NO_3)_2$ _____   (d) AgI _____

(e) $BaSO_4$ _____   (f) $CaCO_3$ _____

(g) $CuCrO_4$ _____   (h) $AlPO_4$ _____

(i) ZnS _____   (j) $Sr(OH)_2$ _____

4. Write a balanced chemical equation for each of the following reactions.

(a) potassium(s) + chlorine(g) $\xrightarrow{\Delta}$ potassium chloride(s)

(b) calcium carbonate(s) $\xrightarrow{\Delta}$ calcium oxide(s) + carbon dioxide(g)

(c) lithium metal(s) + water(l) $\rightarrow$ lithium hydroxide(aq) + hydrogen(g)

(d) lead(II) nitrate(aq) + sodium iodide (aq) $\rightarrow$ lead(II) iodide(s) + sodium nitrate(aq)

(e) acetic acid(aq) + barium hydroxide(aq) $\rightarrow$ barium acetate(aq) + water(l)

5. (optional) A 1980 penny weighing 3.079 g reacts with nitric acid to give a blue solution. An electric current is passed through the solution and 2.925 g of copper metal is produced. What is the percentage of copper in the 1980 penny?

_____

ANSWERS TO PRELABORATORY ASSIGNMENTS

1. See the Glossary.
2. (a) combination, (b) decomposition, (c) single replacement, (d) double replacement, (e) neutralization
3. (a) a gas is released; (b) a precipitate is produced; (c) a permanent color change is observed; (d) an energy change is noted, such as heat or light.
4. (a) (g); (b) (l); (c) (s); (d) (aq); (e) (s); (f) Δ; (g) *NR*
5. (a) colorless; (b) pink
6. The 1980 mint date cannot be used as it is a "copper penny."
7. (a) 2.5% Cu; (b) 97.48% Zn
8. • Wear safety goggles; be careful when using the laboratory burner.
   • Handle chemicals carefully, and avoid breathing the vapors of hydrochloric acid.
   • Dispose of chemical waste in the designated container.

Decomposing Baking Soda

OBJECTIVES

- To determine the percent yield of sodium carbonate from a decomposition reaction.
- To determine the percentage of sodium hydrogen carbonate in an unknown mixture.
- To gain proficiency in decomposing a compound and collecting a gas over water.

DISCUSSION

When baking soda is heated, sodium hydrogen carbonate, $NaHCO_3$, decomposes into solid sodium carbonate, while releasing steam and carbon dioxide gas. The equation for the reaction is

$$2\ NaHCO_3(s) \xrightarrow{\Delta} Na_2CO_3(s) + H_2O(g) + CO_2(g)$$

Notice that the reaction releases H_2O and CO_2 as gases but Na_2CO_3 remains a solid. If we *weigh* the mass of solid Na_2CO_3 produced in an experiment, the mass is referred to as the **actual yield**. Conversely, if we *calculate* the mass of Na_2CO_3 according to the balanced chemical equation, the mass is referred to as the **theoretical yield**.

The **percent yield** from a chemical reaction is an expression for the amount of actual yield compared to the theoretical yield. While some experimental errors give high results, other errors give low results. Thus, the percent yield can be greater than—or less than—100%.

From Experiment 14 of *Laboratory Manual to Accompany Introductory Chemistry: Concepts and Critical Thinking*, Sixth Edition. Charles H. Corwin. Copyright © 2013 by Pearson Education, Inc. All rights reserved.

Percent Yield of Sodium Carbonate from Baking Soda

Example Exercise 1 • % Yield of Na_2CO_3 from Baking Soda

A 1.654-g sample of pure baking soda, $NaHCO_3$, decomposes to produce 1.028 g of solid sodium carbonate. Calculate the theoretical yield and percent yield of Na_2CO_3.

Solution: According to the balanced equation, 2 mol $NaHCO_3$ (84.01 g/mol) produce 1 mol Na_2CO_3 (105.99 g/mol). We can find the theoretical yield as follows:

$$1.654 \text{ g NaHCO}_3 \times \frac{1 \text{ mol NaHCO}_3}{84.01 \text{ g NaHCO}_3} \times \frac{1 \text{ mol Na}_2\text{CO}_3}{2 \text{ mol NaHCO}_3} \times \frac{105.99 \text{ g Na}_2\text{CO}_3}{1 \text{ mol Na}_2\text{CO}_3}$$

$$= 1.043 \text{ g Na}_2\text{CO}_3$$

Since the actual yield of Na_2CO_3 is 1.028 g, the percent yield is

$$\frac{\text{actual yield}}{\text{theoretical yield}} \times 100\% = \% \text{ yield}$$

$$\frac{1.028 \text{ g}}{1.043 \text{ g}} \times 100\% = 98.56\%$$

Percentage of Sodium Hydrogen Carbonate in an Unknown Mixture

An unknown mixture containing baking soda is decomposed using heat. The following example exercise illustrates the calculation for the percentage of baking soda in the mixture.

Example Exercise 2 • % $NaHCO_3$ in an Unknown Mixture

A 1.675-g unknown mixture containing baking soda is decomposed with heat. If the mass loss is 0.318 g, what is the percentage of baking soda, $NaHCO_3$, in the unknown mixture?

Solution: In this example, the mass loss corresponds to both the mass of water vapor and carbon dioxide gas. To simplify the calculation, we will combine H_2O + CO_2 into H_2CO_3 (62.03 g/mol) and rewrite the chemical equation.

$$2 \text{ NaHCO}_3(s) \xrightarrow{\Delta} \text{Na}_2\text{CO}_3(s) + \text{H}_2\text{CO}_3(g)$$

We can relate the H_2CO_3 mass loss to the mass of $NaHCO_3$ as follows:

$$0.318 \text{ g H}_2\text{CO}_3 \times \frac{1 \text{ mol H}_2\text{CO}_3}{62.03 \text{ g H}_2\text{CO}_3} \times \frac{2 \text{ mol NaHCO}_3}{1 \text{ mol H}_2\text{CO}_3} \times \frac{84.01 \text{ g NaHCO}_3}{1 \text{ mol NaHCO}_3}$$

$$= 0.861 \text{ g NaHCO}_3$$

If the sample mixture has a mass of 1.675 g, the percentage of $NaHCO_3$ is

$$\frac{\text{mass NaHCO}_3}{\text{mass sample}} \times 100\% = \% \text{ NaHCO}_3$$

$$\frac{0.861 \text{ g}}{1.675 \text{ g}} \times 100\% = 51.4\%$$

Figure 1 shows the experimental apparatus for decomposing baking soda. As the baking soda decomposes, carbon dioxide gas is produced. The carbon dioxide gas displaces water from the Florence flask into the 1000-mL beaker. When the decomposition is complete, no more carbon dioxide gas is released and the water level in the beaker remains constant.

Using a gas collection apparatus shown in 1 provides a visual learning experience for collecting a gas over water. That is, the carbon dioxide gas released from heating baking soda displaces water from the Florence flask into the beaker, If the apparatus is not readily available, this experiment can be performed by heating baking soda in a crucible and cover.

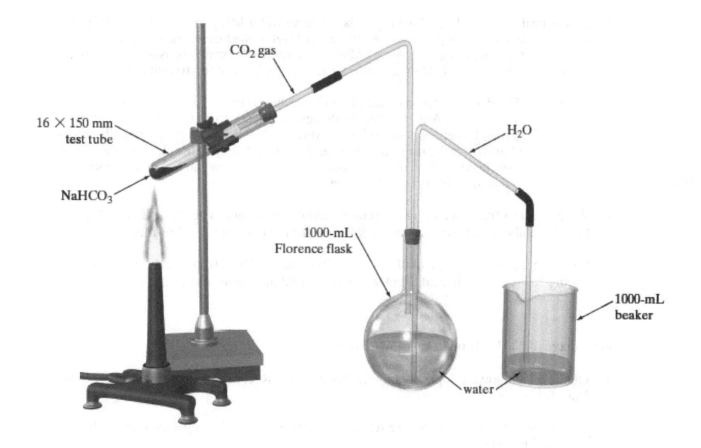

CO$_2$ gas

16 × 150 mm test tube

NaHCO$_3$

1000-mL Florence flask

H$_2$O

1000-mL beaker

water

Figure 1 Decomposition Apparatus When the water level in the beaker remains constant, the decomposition of NaHCO$_3$ is complete.

EQUIPMENT and CHEMICALS

- gas collection apparatus (see Figure 1)
- 16 x 150 mm test tube
- 1000-mL Florence flask
- 1000-mL beaker

- sodium hydrogen carbonate, baking soda, solid NaHCO$_3$
- unknown baking soda mixture, 50–90% NaHCO$_3$

PROCEDURE

A. Percent Yield of Na_2CO_3 from Baking Soda

1. Weigh a 16 x 150 mm *dry* test tube on the balance, and record the mass. Add 1–2 g of baking soda, $NaHCO_3$, and reweigh.

2. Set up the apparatus as shown in Figure 1. Fill the Florence flask to the neck with tap water, and insert the gas collection apparatus. Insert the small rubber stopper into the test tube as shown.

3. Gently heat the test tube and baking soda. Observe water being displaced into the beaker as carbon dioxide gas is produced. As the water level in the beaker increases, continue to heat the test tube with a gentle flame. After the water level remains constant for a couple of minutes, discontinue heating and allow the test tube to cool for 10 minutes.

   Note: The decomposition of baking soda produces steam that may collect in the test tube. Any moisture in the test tube leads to serious weighing errors. If there appears to be moisture in the test tube, remove the utility clamp from the ring stand and carefully heat the open test tube over a low flame until no trace of moisture remains. Allow the test tube to cool for 10 minutes before weighing.

RECYCLE
Chemical
Waste

4. Weigh the test tube containing the sodium carbonate residue. The mass of Na_2CO_3 is found by subtracting the mass of the test tube from the test tube and residue.

5. Calculate the theoretical yield of sodium carbonate, Na_2CO_3, from the mass of pure baking soda that was heated. Find the percent yield of sodium carbonate.

B. Percentage of $NaHCO_3$ in an Unknown Mixture

1. Obtain an unknown sample containing baking soda. Record the unknown number in the Data Table.

2. Repeat steps 1–5 as in Procedure A; substitute an unknown baking soda mixture for pure baking soda.

3. Calculate the mass of baking soda, $NaHCO_3$, in the unknown sample from the mass loss. Find the percentage of baking soda in the unknown mixture.

EXPERIMENT   NAME _____

DATE _____   SECTION _____

PRELABORATORY ASSIGNMENT*

1. Provide the key term that corresponds to each of the following definitions.

_____ (a) the relationship of quantities (i.e., mass of substance or volume of gas) in a chemical reaction according to the balanced chemical equation

_____ (b) the mass of 1 mole of any substance expressed in grams

_____ (c) a procedure for obtaining the mass of a sample by first weighing a container and then weighing the container with the sample

_____ (d) a technique for determining the volume of a gas by measuring the volume of water it displaces

_____ (e) the amount of product experimentally obtained from a reaction

_____ (f) the amount of product that is calculated from a given amount of reactant

_____ (g) the actual yield compared to the theoretical yield expressed as a percent

   Key Terms: actual yield, molar mass (MM), percent yield, stoichiometry, theoretical yield, volume by displacement, weighing by difference

2. How do you tell when the baking soda sample is decomposed completely?

3. Is it possible to obtain a percent yield of Na_2CO_3 that is greater than 100%?

4. What are major sources of experimental error?

_____

* Answers at the end of the experiment.

5. A 1.555-g sample of baking soda decomposes with heat to produce 0.991 g Na_2CO_3. Refer to Example Exercise 1 and show the calculation for the theoretical yield of Na_2CO_3.

_____

What is the percent yield of sodium carbonate, Na_2CO_3?

_____

6. A 1.473-g unknown mixture with baking soda is heated and has a mass loss of 0.325 g. Refer to Example Exercise 2 and show the calculation for the percentage $NaHCO_3$ in the mixture.

_____

7. What safety precautions must be observed in this experiment?

EXPERIMENT _____   NAME _____

DATE _____   SECTION _____

DATA TABLE

A. Percent Yield of Na_2CO_3 from Baking Soda

mass of test tube + $NaHCO_3$ _____ g   _____ g
(before heating)

mass of test tube   _____ g   _____ g

mass of $NaHCO_3$ _____ g   _____ g

mass of test tube + Na_2CO_3 _____ g   _____ g
(after heating)

mass of Na_2CO_3 *(actual yield)*   _____ g   _____ g
(after heating – test tube)

RECYCLE
Chemical
Waste

Show the calculation for theoretical yield of Na_2CO_3 for trial 1 (see Example Exercise 1).

mass of Na_2CO_3 *(theoretical yield)*   _____ g   _____ g

Show the calculation for percent yield of Na_2CO_3 for trial 1 (see Example Exercise 1).

Percent Yield of Na_2CO_3 _____ %   _____ %

Average Percent Yield   _____ %

113

B. Percentage of NaHCO₃ in an Unknown Mixture   **UNKNOWN #** _____

mass of test tube + unknown mixture   _____ g   _____ g
(before heating)

mass of test tube   _____ g   _____ g

mass of unknown mixture   _____ g   _____ g

mass of test tube + residue   _____ g   _____ g
(after heating)

mass of H_2CO_3 $(H_2O + CO_2)$ _____ g   _____ g
(before heating – after heating)

Show the calculation for the mass of NaHCO₃ in the unknown mixture for trial 1 (see Example Exercise 2).

mass of NaHCO₃   _____ g   _____ g

Show the calculation for the percentage of NaHCO₃ in the unknown mixture for trial 1 (see Example Exercise 2).

Percentage of NaHCO₃   _____ %   _____ %

Average percentage of NaHCO₃   _____ %

RECYCLE
Chemical
Waste

EXPERIMENT

NAME _____

DATE _____

SECTION _____

POSTLABORATORY ASSIGNMENT

1. A 1.225-g sample of pure lithium hydrogen carbonate is decomposed by heating to produce 0.660 g lithium carbonate. Calculate the theoretical yield and percent yield of Li_2CO_3.

$$2\ LiHCO_3(s) \xrightarrow{\Delta} Li_2CO_3(s)\ +\ H_2O(g)\ +\ CO_2(g)$$

_____

_____

2. A 1.205-g sample mixture of lithium hydrogen carbonate is decomposed by heating. If the mass loss is 0.275 g, what is the percentage of $LiHCO_3$ in the unknown mixture?

$$2\ LiHCO_3(s) \xrightarrow{\Delta} Li_2CO_3(s)\ +\ H_2CO_3(g)$$

_____

3. Lithium chlorate is decomposed with heat to give lithium chloride and oxygen gas. If 1.115 g of lithium chlorate is decomposed, how many milliliters of oxygen gas is released at STP?

$$2 \, LiClO_3(s) \quad \xrightarrow{\Delta} \quad 2 \, LiCl(s) \; + \; 3 \, O_2(g)$$

_____

4. Lithium metal reacts with water to give lithium hydroxide and hydrogen gas. If 75.5 mL of hydrogen gas is produced at STP, what is the mass of lithium metal that reacted?

$$2 \, Li(s) \; + \; 2 \, H_2O(l) \quad \rightarrow \quad 2 \, LiOH(aq) \; + \; H_2(g)$$

_____

5. (optional) The Solvay process is used to manufacture baking soda, $NaHCO_3$. In the process, CO_2, NH_3, H_2O, and NaCl react to produce baking soda. If 25.0 L CO_2 and 20.0 L NH_3 react at STP, with excess water and sodium chloride, what is the limiting reactant? Calculate the mass of baking soda produced.

$$CO_2(g) \; + \; NH_3(g) \; + \; H_2O(l) \; + \; NaCl(s) \quad \rightarrow \quad NaHCO_3(s) \; + \; NH_4Cl(aq)$$

Limiting Reactant _____   Mass $NaHCO_3$ _____

ANSWERS TO PRELABORATORY ASSIGNMENTS

1. See the Glossary.
2. The baking soda is decomposed completely when carbon dioxide gas is no longer produced, and the water level in the beaker remains constant.
3. Yes, some errors can lead to high results, giving a percent yield greater than 100%.
4. • Heating the baking soda mixture insufficiently gives high results.
   • Weighing a test tube with traces of moisture gives a heavy mass reading.
   • Weighing a test tube while warm gives a light mass reading.
5. 0.991 g; (0.991 g / 0.981 g) x 100% = 101%
6. (0.880 g / 1.473 g) x 100% = 60.0%
7. • Wear safety goggles; be careful when using the laboratory burner.
   • Heat the samples in a test tube slowly and carefully.
   • Avoid pinching the rubber tubing from the test tube to the Florence flask.
   • Dispose of chemical waste in the designated container.

Generating Hydrogen Gas

OBJECTIVES

- To determine the experimental molar volume of hydrogen gas at STP.
- To determine the atomic mass and identity for an unknown metal (**X**).
- To gain experience in collecting a gas over water and reading a barometer.

DISCUSSION

The **molar volume** of a gas is the volume occupied by one mole of gas at standard conditions. The theoretical value for the molar volume of an ideal gas at **standard temperature and pressure (STP)** is 22.4 liters. A volume of 22.4 L contains Avogadro's number of molecules. The molar volume concept is illustrated in Figure 1.

Figure 1 The Mole Concept One mole of gas occupies 22.4 L at STP, and contains Avogadro's number of molecules.

From Experiment 16 of *Laboratory Manual to Accompany Introductory Chemistry: Concepts and Critical Thinking*, Sixth Edition. Charles H. Corwin.

Molar Volume of Hydrogen Gas

In this experiment, magnesium metal reacts with hydrochloric acid according to the equation

$$Mg(s) \quad + \quad 2\,HCl(aq) \quad \rightarrow \quad MgCl_2(aq) \quad + \quad H_2(g)$$

We can find an experimental value for the molar volume of hydrogen gas from the stoichiometry of the reaction. The following example exercise illustrates the calculation of molar volume.

Example Exercise 1 • Molar Volume of Hydrogen Gas

A 0.0750 g sample of magnesium metal reacts with hydrochloric acid to produce 77.5 mL of hydrogen gas. The "wet" gas is collected over water at 20 °C and an atmospheric pressure of 763 mm Hg. Calculate the experimental molar volume of hydrogen gas at STP.

Solution: Since the gas is collected over water, both hydrogen gas and water vapor contribute to the total pressure. We find in Table 1 the **vapor pressure** of water at 20 °C is 18 mm Hg. The total pressure of the hydrogen gas and water vapor equals the **atmospheric pressure**, that is, 763 mm Hg. Applying **Dalton's law of partial pressures** we have

$$
\begin{aligned}
P_{H_2} + P_{H_2O} &= P_{atm} \\
P_{H_2} + 18 \text{ mm Hg} &= 763 \text{ mm Hg} \\
P_{H_2} &= 763 \text{ mm Hg} - 18 \text{ mm Hg} \\
&= 745 \text{ mm Hg}
\end{aligned}
$$

Let's prepare a table for the pressure, volume, and temperature data.

Conditions	P	V	T
initial	745 mm Hg	77.5 mL	20 + 273 = 293 K
final	760 mm Hg	V_{STP}	0 + 273 = 273 K

We can correct the volume of H_2 gas to STP using the **combined gas law**.

$$V_{initial} \quad \times \quad P_{factor} \quad \times \quad T_{factor} \quad = \quad V_{STP}$$

The pressure increases, so the volume decreases. The P_{factor} is less than 1. The temperature decreases, so the volume decreases. The T_{factor} is less than 1.

$$77.5 \text{ mL } H_2 \quad \times \quad \frac{745 \text{ mm Hg}}{760 \text{ mm Hg}} \quad \times \quad \frac{273 \text{ K}}{293 \text{ K}} \quad = \quad 70.8 \text{ mL } H_2$$

Referring to the above balanced chemical equation, we see that 1 mol Mg metal produces 1 mol H_2 gas; thus,

$$0.0750 \text{ g Mg} \quad \times \quad \frac{1 \text{ mol Mg}}{24.31 \text{ g Mg}} \quad \times \quad \frac{1 \text{ mol } H_2}{1 \text{ mol Mg}} \quad = \quad 0.00309 \text{ mol } H_2$$

The molar volume is the ratio of liters of H_2 gas at STP to moles of H_2 gas produced from the reaction. Thus,

$$\frac{70.8 \text{ mL } H_2}{0.00309 \text{ mol } H_2} \quad \times \quad \frac{1 \text{ L}}{1000 \text{ mL}} \quad = \quad 22.9 \text{ L/mol}$$

The experimental molar volume is 22.9 L/mol at STP. This value compares closely with the theoretical molar volume of 22.4 L/mol.

Atomic Mass of an Unknown Metal

After reacting magnesium metal and hydrochloric acid, we will react an unknown metal (X) in a similar fashion. The equation for the reaction is

$$X(s) \ + \ 2 \text{ HCl(aq)} \ \rightarrow \ XCl_2(aq) \ + \ H_2(g)$$

We can use the concept of molar volume to calculate the atomic mass of the unknown metal as shown in the following example exercise.

Example Exercise 2 • Atomic Mass of an Unknown Metal

A 0.215-g sample of unknown metal produces 81.0 mL of hydrogen gas. The "wet" gas is collected over water at 21 °C and an atmospheric pressure of 763 mm Hg. Calculate the atomic mass of the unknown metal (X).

Solution: We find in Table 1 that the vapor pressure of water at 21 °C is 19 mm Hg. The partial pressure of hydrogen gas is found by applying Dalton's law.

$$\begin{aligned} P_{H_2} + P_{H_2O} \ &= \ P_{atm} \\ P_{H_2} + 19 \text{ mm Hg} \ &= \ 763 \text{ mm Hg} \\ P_{H_2} \ &= \ 763 \text{ mm Hg} - 19 \text{ mm Hg} \\ &= \ 744 \text{ mm Hg} \end{aligned}$$

Let's prepare a table for the pressure, volume, and temperature data.

Conditions	P	V	T
initial	744 mm Hg	81.0 mL	21 + 273 = 294 K
final	760 mm Hg	V_{STP}	0 + 273 = 273 K

We can correct the initial volume of H_2 gas to STP conditions as follows:

$$81.0 \text{ mL } H_2 \quad \times \quad P_{factor} \quad \times \quad T_{factor} \quad = \quad V_{STP}$$

The pressure increases, so the volume decreases. The P_{factor} is less than 1. The temperature decreases, and volume decreases. The T_{factor} is less than 1.

Since the pressure and temperature factors are less than 1, we have

$$81.0 \text{ mL H}_2 \quad \times \quad \frac{744 \text{ mm Hg}}{760 \text{ mm Hg}} \quad \times \quad \frac{273 \text{ K}}{294 \text{ K}} \quad = \quad 73.6 \text{ mL H}_2$$

According to the balanced equation for the reaction, 1 mole of unknown metal (**X**) produces 1 mole of hydrogen gas. Thus, at STP

$$73.6 \text{ mL H}_2 \quad \times \quad \frac{1 \text{ L}}{1000 \text{ mL}} \quad \times \quad \frac{1 \text{ mol H}_2}{22.4 \text{ L H}_2} \quad \times \quad \frac{1 \text{ mol X}}{1 \text{ mol H}_2} \quad = \quad 0.00329 \text{ mol X}$$

The atomic mass of the unknown metal is expressed by the ratio of the mass of sample to the moles of metal.

$$\frac{0.215 \text{ g X}}{0.00329 \text{ mol X}} \quad = \quad 65.3 \text{ g/mol}$$

The atomic mass of the unknown metal (**X**) is 65.3 g/mol. If we refer to the periodic table, we identify the unknown metal as zinc (65.39 g/mol).

In this experiment, we will collect hydrogen gas over water. The hydrogen gas displaces water from a graduated cylinder. Figure 2 illustrates an apparatus for collecting the gas.

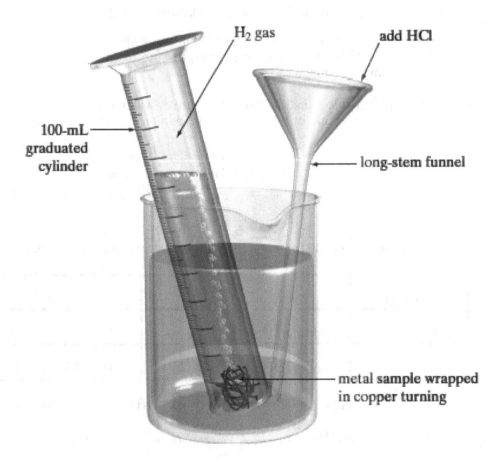

Figure 2 Gas Collection Apparatus The volume of hydrogen gas produced equals the volume of water displaced from the graduated cylinder.

EQUIPMENT and CHEMICALS

- 1000-mL beaker
- 100-mL graduated cylinder
- wash bottle with distilled water
- long-stem funnel
- 100-mL beaker
- 110 °C thermometer
- barometer
- milligram balances
- tenth milligram balances (optional)

- magnesium, Mg ribbon
- copper, Cu light turnings
- dilute hydrochloric acid, 6 M HCl
- unknown metal samples (**X**)

PROCEDURE

A. Molar Volume of Hydrogen Gas

1. Cut a strip of magnesium ribbon with a 0.070–0.090 g mass (approximately 7–9 cm). Weigh the magnesium metal. Roll the metal ribbon into a compact coil and wrap with strands of copper turnings.

2. Add 700 mL of water into a 1000-mL beaker. Drop the copper-wrapped magnesium metal into the water.

3. Fill a 100-mL graduated cylinder with water. Adjust the water level to the upper rim using water from a wash bottle. Place a small piece of paper towel over the entire rim, and allow it to absorb water. Invert the graduated cylinder over the sink. Carefully put the graduated cylinder into the beaker. As the piece of towel floats free, place the graduated cylinder over the copper-wrapped metal as shown in Figure 2.

   Note: It is advisable to practice inverting the graduated cylinder filled with water. If the graduated cylinder loses water upon inversion, the paper towel may be too large. On occasion, the spout in the graduated cylinder is too deep. Exchanging the graduated cylinder solves this problem.

4. Using a long-stem funnel, add 25 mL of dilute hydrochloric acid into the beaker. Gas bubbles are observed when the acid reacts with the magnesium sample. When the reaction is complete, tilt the cylinder vertically and read the bottom of the meniscus. Record the volume (± 0.5 mL) in the Data Table.

   RECYCLE
   Chemical
   Waste

5. Place the thermometer into the beaker of water, and observe the temperature. Record the temperature of the hydrogen gas in the Data Table.

   Note: Since the hydrogen gas is collected over water, the temperature of the hydrogen gas is the same as the temperature of the water in the beaker.

6. Read the barometer, and record the atmospheric pressure. Find the vapor pressure of water from Table 1.

7. Calculate the molar volume of hydrogen gas at STP.

Table 1 Vapor Pressure of Water

Temperature	Pressure	Temperature	Pressure	Temperature	Pressure
16 °C	14 mm Hg	21 °C	19 mm Hg	26 °C	25 mm Hg
17 °C	15 mm Hg	22 °C	20 mm Hg	27 °C	27 mm Hg
18 °C	16 mm Hg	23 °C	21 mm Hg	28 °C	28 mm Hg
19 °C	17 mm Hg	24 °C	22 mm Hg	29 °C	30 mm Hg
20 °C	18 mm Hg	25 °C	24 mm Hg	30 °C	32 mm Hg

B. Atomic Mass of an Unknown Metal

RECYCLE
Chemical
Waste

1. Obtain a sample of unknown metal (**X**), and record the number in the Data Table.

2. Follow the same steps as in Procedure A.

3. Calculate the atomic mass of the unknown metal (**X**). Refer to the atomic masses in the periodic table, and identify the unknown metal (**X**).

EXPERIMENT

DATE _____

NAME _____

SECTION _____

PRELABORATORY ASSIGNMENT*

1. Provide the key term that corresponds to each of the following definitions.

    _____ (a) the relationship of quantities (i.e., mass of substance or volume of gas) in a chemical reaction according to the balanced chemical equation

    _____ (b) the volume occupied by 1 mole of any gas at STP

    _____ (c) a temperature of 273 K and a pressure of 760 mm Hg for a gas

    _____ (d) the pressure exerted by air molecules in Earth's atmosphere

    _____ (e) the pressure exerted by gaseous vapor above a liquid in a closed container when the rates of evaporation and condensation are equal

    _____ (f) the pressure exerted by a mixture of gases is equal to the sum of the pressures exerted by each gas in the mixture

    _____ (g) the pressure exerted by a gas is inversely proportional to its volume and directly proportional to its Kelvin temperature

    _____ (h) a technique for determining the volume of a gas by measuring the volume of water it displaces

    Key Terms: atmospheric pressure, combined gas law, Dalton's law, molar volume, standard temperature and pressure, stoichiometry, vapor pressure, volume by displacement

2. Why does the graduated cylinder remain full of water after inverting?

3. Why must the mass of magnesium be less than 0.09 g in this experiment?

4. How do you tell when the magnesium metal has reacted completely?

5. Explain the meaning of the following terms:

    (a) "wet gas"

    (b) "dry gas"

_____

* Answers at the end of the experiment.

6. Hydrogen gas is collected over water at 25 °C and an atmospheric pressure of 766 mm Hg. Refer to Table 1 and show the calculation for the partial pressure of hydrogen gas.

7. A 0.0795-g sample of magnesium metal reacts with hydrochloric acid to give 88.5 mL of hydrogen gas at 25 °C and 766 mm Hg. Refer to Example Exercise 1 and show the calculation for the volume of hydrogen gas at STP.

Calculate the moles of hydrogen gas produced.

Calculate the molar volume of hydrogen gas at STP.

8. What are major sources of experimental error?

9. What safety precautions should be observed in this experiment?

EXPERIMENT

NAME _____

DATE _____

SECTION _____

DATA TABLE

A. Molar Volume of Hydrogen Gas

mass of magnesium _____ g _____ g

volume of hydrogen gas _____ mL _____ mL

temperature of hydrogen gas _____ °C _____ °C

atmospheric pressure (see barometer) _____ mm Hg _____ mm Hg

vapor pressure of water (see Table 1) _____ mm Hg _____ mm Hg

partial pressure of hydrogen gas _____ mm Hg _____ mm Hg

Correct the volume of hydrogen gas to STP for trial 1 (see Example Exercise 1).

RECYCLE
Chemical
Waste

volume of hydrogen gas (STP) _____ mL _____ mL

Show the calculation for the moles of hydrogen gas for trial 1 (see Example Exercise 1).

moles of hydrogen gas _____ mol _____ mol

Show the calculation for the molar volume of hydrogen gas at STP for trial 1.

Molar volume of hydrogen gas (STP) _____ L/mol _____ L/mol

B. Atomic Mass of an Unknown Metal   **UNKNOWN #** _____

mass of metal (**X**)   _____ g   _____ g

volume of hydrogen gas   _____ mL   _____ mL

temperature of hydrogen gas   _____ °C   _____ °C

    atmospheric pressure (see barometer)   _____ mm Hg   _____ mm Hg

    vapor pressure of water (see Table 1) _____ mm Hg   _____ mm Hg

partial pressure of hydrogen gas   _____ mm Hg   _____ mm Hg

Correct the volume of hydrogen gas to STP for trial 1 (see Example Exercise 2).

RECYCLE
Chemical
Waste

volume of hydrogen gas (STP)   _____ mL   _____ mL

Show the calculation for moles of unknown metal (**X**) for trial 1 (see Example Exercise 2).

moles of unknown metal   _____ mol   _____ mol

Show the calculation for the atomic mass of the unknown metal (**X**) for trial 1.

Atomic mass of the unknown metal (**X**)   _____ g/mol   _____ g/mol

Identity of the unknown metal (**X**)   _____   _____

EXPERIMENT   NAME _____

DATE _____   SECTION _____

POSTLABORATORY ASSIGNMENT

1. A 0.200-g sample of cobalt metal reacted with hydrochloric acid according to the following balanced chemical equation:

$$Co(s) \quad + \quad 2\,HCl(aq) \quad \rightarrow \quad CoCl_2(aq) \quad + \quad H_2(g)$$

The volume of hydrogen gas collected over water was 87.5 mL at 20 °C and a barometer reading of 763 mm Hg. Calculate the STP molar volume for hydrogen.

_____ L/mol

2. A 0.130-g sample of an unknown metal (**X**) reacted with hydrochloric acid according to the following chemical equation:

$$2\,X(s) \quad + \quad 6\,HCl(aq) \quad \rightarrow \quad 2\,XCl_3(aq) \quad + \quad 3\,H_2(g)$$

The volume of hydrogen gas collected over water was 92.0 mL at 20 °C and 763 mm Hg. Calculate the atomic mass of the unknown metal and identify the metal from the periodic table.

_____ g/mol

_____ (**X**)

3. A barometer reads 775 mm Hg. Express the atmospheric pressure in the following units.

   (a) atm

   (b) cm Hg

   (c) in. Hg

4. Applying Boyle's Law Concept:
   As a piston compresses air in a cylinder, the gas pressure (increases/decreases).

5. Applying Charles's Law Concept:
   As a rubber balloon cools in a freezer, the volume (increases/decreases).

6. Applying Gay-Lussac's Law Concept:
   As an automobile tire rolls along the highway, the tire pressure (increases/decreases).

7. (optional) Argon gas has a boiling point of –197 °C. Which of the following diagrams best represents the distribution of argon atoms in a steel sphere at –190 °C?

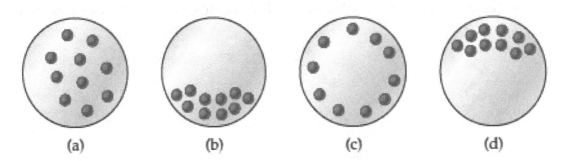

   (a)   (b)   (c)   (d)

ANSWERS TO PRELABORATORY ASSIGNMENTS

1. See the Glossary.
2. The graduated cylinder remains full of water after inverting due to atmospheric pressure.
3. If the magnesium weighs more than 0.09 g, the metal produces more than 100 mL of gas, which exceeds the capacity of the graduated cylinder.
4. The reaction is complete when the metal disappears and gas bubbles are no longer observed.
5. A "wet gas" is collected over water and contains water vapor; a "dry gas" gas does not. To obtain the partial pressure of a "dry gas," subtract the vapor pressure of water from the atmospheric pressure at experimental conditions.
6. The partial pressure of a "dry gas" equals the atmospheric pressure minus vapor pressure. Table 1 lists the vapor pressure at 25 °C as 24 mm Hg. Therefore, the partial pressure of "dry" hydrogen gas is 766 mm Hg – 24 mm Hg = 742 mm Hg.
7. 79.2 mL H_2 at STP; 0.00327 mol H_2 at STP; 24.2 L/mol
8. The major sources of error in this experiment include:
   • a large air bubble in the graduated cylinder, after inverting the cylinder filled with water
   • incomplete reaction of the metal
   • misreading the meniscus in the graduated cylinder
9. • Wear safety goggles; be careful with the glassware when collecting the gas.
   • Handle hydrochloric acid carefully, and avoid breathing the vapor.
   • Handle the thermometer carefully, as it is easily broken.
     (Report a broken thermometer immediately to the Instructor; mercury vapor is hazardous.)
   • Dispose of chemical waste in the designated container.

Electrical Conductivity of Aqueous Solutions

OBJECTIVES

- To observe the electrical conductivity of substances in aqueous solution.
- To determine whether an aqueous solution is a strong or weak electrolyte.
- To interpret a chemical reaction by observing aqueous solution conductivity.
- To become proficient in writing net ionic equations.

DISCUSSION

Electrical conductivity is based on the flow of electrons. Metals are good conductors of electricity because they allow electrons to flow through the metal. Distilled water is a very weak conductor because very little electricity passes through pure water. However, when a substance dissolves in water and forms ions, the ions are capable of conducting an electric current. If the substance is highly ionized, the solution is a strong conductor of electricity. If the substance is only slightly ionized, the solution is a weak conductor.

Soluble salts dissolve in water to form positive and negative ions. For example, sodium chloride dissolves in water to form Na^+ and Cl^- ions. The separation of ions in an ionic compound is termed **dissociation**.

A strong acid also dissolves in water to form positive and negative ions. For example, hydrogen chloride dissolves in water to form H^+ and Cl^- ions. The formation of positive and negative ions from a molecular compound, such as HCl, is termed **ionization**.

From Experiment 21 of *Laboratory Manual to Accompany Introductory Chemistry: Concepts and Critical Thinking*, Sixth Edition. Charles H. Corwin.

In this experiment, you will be testing conductivity using an apparatus that has two wires serving as electrodes (Figure 1). If the electrodes are immersed in a strong electrolyte solution, the circuit is completed and the light bulb in the apparatus glows brightly. If the electrodes are immersed in a weak electrolyte solution, the light bulb glows dimly.

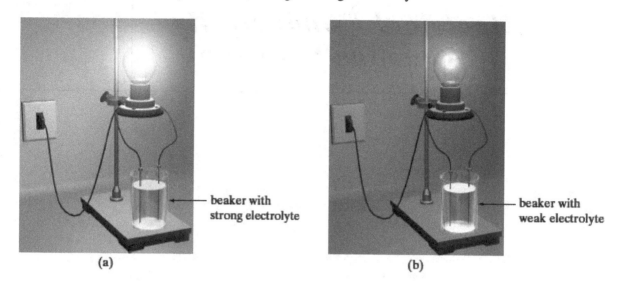

(a)　　　　　　　　　　　　　　　　(b)

Figure 1 Apparatus for Conductivity Testing (a) A strong electrolyte is a good conductor of electricity and the light bulb glows brightly. (b) A weak electrolyte is a poor conductor of electricity and the light bulb glows dimly.

A solution that is a good conductor of an electric current is called a **strong electrolyte**. Examples of strong electrolytes include strong acids, strong bases, and salts that are highly soluble in aqueous solution. A solution that is a poor conductor of electricity is called a **weak electrolyte**. Examples of weak electrolytes include weak acids, weak bases, and salts that are only slightly soluble in aqueous solution. Table 1 lists several common examples of strong and weak electrolytes.

Table 1 Strong and Weak Electrolytes

Strong Electrolytes	Weak Electrolytes
Strong Acids hydrochloric acid, $HCl(aq)$ nitric acid, $HNO_3(aq)$ sulfuric acid, $H_2SO_4(aq)$	*Weak Acids* hydrofluoric acid, $HF(aq)$ acetic acid, $HC_2H_3O_2(aq)$ most other acids
Strong Bases sodium hydroxide, $NaOH(aq)$ potassium hydroxide, $KOH(aq)$ calcium hydroxide, $Ca(OH)_2(aq)$ barium hydroxide, $Ba(OH)_2(aq)$	*Weak Bases* ammonium hydroxide, $NH_4OH(aq)$ most other bases
Soluble Salts sodium chloride, $NaCl(aq)$ sodium carbonate, $Na_2CO_3(aq)$ sodium sulfate, $Na_2SO_4(aq)$	*Very Slightly Soluble Salts* silver chloride, $AgCl(s)$ calcium carbonate, $CaCO_3(s)$ barium sulfate, $BaSO_4(s)$

Since strong electrolytes are highly ionized, we will indicate these substances as *ionized* in aqueous solution. Conversely, since weak electrolytes are only slightly ionized, we will indicate these substances as *nonionized* in aqueous solution. The following examples illustrate writing strong and weak electrolytes in aqueous solution.

Example 1 • Ionization of a Strong Acid

Sulfuric acid is a strong acid and the light bulb gives a bright glow when tested by the conductivity apparatus. Write H_2SO_4 as it exists in aqueous solution.

Solution: Sulfuric acid is a strong electrolyte that is highly ionized. Thus, we will write aqueous H_2SO_4 as *ionized*: $2 H^+(aq) + SO_4^{2-}(aq)$.

Example 2 • Ionization of a Weak Acid

Carbonic acid is a weak acid and the light bulb gives a dim glow when tested by the conductivity apparatus. Write H_2CO_3 as it exists in aqueous solution.

Solution: Carbonic acid is a weak electrolyte that is only slightly ionized. Thus, we will write aqueous H_2CO_3 as *nonionized*: $H_2CO_3(aq)$.

Example 3 • Ionization of a Strong Base

Potassium hydroxide is a strong base and the light bulb gives a bright glow when tested by the conductivity apparatus. Write KOH as it exists in aqueous solution.

Solution: Potassium hydroxide is a strong electrolyte that is highly ionized. Thus, we will write aqueous KOH as *ionized*: $K^+(aq) + OH^-(aq)$.

Example 4 • Ionization of a Weak Base

Ammonium hydroxide is a weak base and the light bulb gives a dim glow when tested by the conductivity apparatus. Write NH_4OH as it exists in aqueous solution.

Solution: Ammonium hydroxide is a weak electrolyte that is only slightly ionized. Thus, we will write aqueous NH_4OH as *nonionized*: $NH_4OH(aq)$.

Example 5 • Dissociation of a Soluble Salt

Aluminum chloride is a soluble salt and the light bulb gives a bright glow when tested by the conductivity apparatus. Write $AlCl_3$ as it exists in aqueous solution.

Solution: Aluminum chloride is a strong electrolyte that is highly ionized. Thus, we will write aqueous $AlCl_3$ as *ionized*: $Al^{3+}(aq) + 3 Cl^-(aq)$.

Writing Net Ionic Equations

Given the chemical equation for a reaction, balance the equation by inspection. Next, convert the balanced chemical equation into a **net ionic equation**, using the following guidelines.

1. Write a substance in the chemical equation in the ionized form if it is a strong electrolyte. Examples of strong electrolytes include: strong acids, strong bases, and soluble salts. Refer to Table 1 for the most common examples.

2. Write a substance in the chemical equation in the nonionized form if it is a weak electrolyte. Examples of weak electrolytes include weak acids, weak bases, insoluble salts, and water.

3. Write the **total ionic equation** that shows highly ionized substances in the ionic form and weakly ionized substances in the nonionized form.

4. Convert the total ionic equation to a net ionic equation by canceling **spectator ions**. Spectator ions must be identical on both sides of the total ionic equation.

5. Check the net ionic equation for (a) mass balance, and (b) ionic charge balance.

Example 6 • Double Replacement Net Ionic Equation

$$CaCl_2(aq) + K_2CO_3(aq) \rightarrow CaCO_3(s) + 2\ KCl(aq)$$

$$Ca^{2+}(aq) + 2\ \cancel{Cl^-}(aq) + 2\ \cancel{K^+}(aq) + CO_3{}^{2-}(aq) \rightarrow CaCO_3(s) + 2\ \cancel{K^+}(aq) + 2\ \cancel{Cl^-}(aq)$$

$$Ca^{2+}(aq) + CO_3{}^{2-}(aq) \rightarrow CaCO_3(s)$$

Example 7 • Double Replacement Net Ionic Equation

$$2\ AlBr_3(aq) + 3\ MgCl_2(aq) \rightarrow 2\ AlCl_3(aq) + 3\ MgBr_2(aq)$$

$$2\ \cancel{Al^{3+}}(aq) + 6\ \cancel{Br^-}(aq) + 3\ \cancel{Mg^{2+}}(aq) + 6\ \cancel{Cl^-}(aq) \rightarrow$$

$$2\ \cancel{Al^{3+}}(aq) + 6\ \cancel{Cl^-}(aq) + 3\ \cancel{Mg^{2+}}(aq) + 6\ \cancel{Br^-}(aq)$$

All spectator ions; thus, all the ions cancel and there is *No Reaction (NR)*.

Example 8 • Neutralization Net Ionic Equation

$$H_2SO_4(aq) + 2\ NaOH(aq) \rightarrow Na_2SO_4(aq) + 2\ H_2O(l)$$

$$2\ H^+(aq) + \cancel{SO_4{}^{2-}}(aq) + 2\ \cancel{Na^+}(aq) + 2\ OH^-(aq) \rightarrow 2\ \cancel{Na^+}(aq) + \cancel{SO_4{}^{2-}}(aq) + 2\ H_2O(l)$$

$$H^+(aq) + OH^-(aq) \rightarrow H_2O(l)$$

EQUIPMENT and CHEMICALS

- conductivity apparatus
- small, dry beakers (6)
- glass stirring rod
- wash bottle with distilled water
- sodium chloride, solid NaCl
- calcium carbonate, solid $CaCO_3$
- calcium chloride, solid $CaCl_2$
- hydrochloric acid, 0.1 M HCl
- acetic acid, 0.1 M $HC_2H_3O_2$
- nitric acid, 0.1 M HNO_3

- sodium hydroxide, 0.1 M NaOH
- ammonium hydroxide, 0.1 M NH_4OH
- potassium iodide, 0.1 M KI
- aluminum nitrate, 0.1 M $Al(NO_3)_3$
- magnesium hydroxide, sat'd. $Mg(OH)_2$
- copper(II) sulfate, 0.1 M $CuSO_4$
- calcium nitrate, 0.1 M $Ca(NO_3)_2$
- sulfuric acid, 0.1 M H_2SO_4
- barium hydroxide, 0.1 M $Ba(OH)_2$
- straw

PROCEDURE

A. Conductivity Testing—Evidence for Ions in Aqueous Solution

> **Note**: Rinse the electrodes with distilled water after each conductivity test. Record your observations in the Data Table, and state whether the conductivity test indicates a strong electrolyte or weak electrolyte. *(Write strong electrolytes as ions and weak electrolytes as molecules; refer to the LiOH and HNO$_2$ examples in the Data Table.)*

1. Pour about 25 mL of *distilled* water in a small dry beaker and test the conductivity. Pour about 25 mL of *tap* water in a small dry beaker and test the conductivity.

2. Place about 0.5 g of solid NaCl in a small dry beaker and test the conductivity. Add distilled water, stir, and retest the conductivity.

3. Place about 0.5 g of solid $CaCO_3$ in a small dry beaker and test the conductivity. Add distilled water, stir, and retest the conductivity.

4. Place about 0.5 g of solid $CaCl_2$ in a small dry beaker and test the conductivity. Add distilled water, stir, and retest the conductivity.

5. Test the conductivity of each of the following in a small beaker:
   (a) ~10 mL hydrochloric acid, 0.1 M HCl
   (b) ~10 mL acetic acid, 0.1 M $HC_2H_3O_2$
   (c) ~10 mL nitric acid, 0.1 M HNO_3
   (d) ~10 mL sodium hydroxide, 0.1 M NaOH
   (e) ~10 mL ammonium hydroxide, 0.1 M NH_4OH
   (f) ~10 mL potassium iodide, 0.1 M KI
   (g) ~10 mL aluminum nitrate, 0.1 M $Al(NO_3)_3$
   (h) ~10 mL magnesium hydroxide, saturated $Mg(OH)_2$
   (i) ~10 mL copper(II) sulfate, 0.1 M $CuSO_4$
   (j) ~10 mL calcium nitrate, 0.1 M $Ca(NO_3)_2$

RECYCLE
Chemical
Waste

B. Conductivity Testing—Evidence for a Chemical Reaction

1. Test the conductivity of 0.1 M $HC_2H_3O_2$ and 0.1 M NH_4OH in separate beakers. Pour the solutions together and retest the conductivity. Record your observations and conclusions in the Data Table. Balance the equation for the reaction, and write the total ionic and net ionic equations.

RECYCLE
Chemical
Waste

2. Test the conductivity of 0.1 M H_2SO_4 and 0.1 M $Ba(OH)_2$ in separate beakers. Add 10 drops of 0.1 M H_2SO_4 into a beaker containing ~25 mL of distilled water. Continuously test the conductivity while adding 0.1 M $Ba(OH)_2$ dropwise until the conductivity is minimal. Record your observations and conclusions. Balance the equation for the reaction, and write the total ionic and net ionic equations.

3. Test the conductivity of distilled water while blowing CO_2 through a straw in the water. Add 10 drops of 0.1 M $Ba(OH)_2$ into a beaker containing ~25 mL of distilled water. Continuously test the conductivity while blowing through a straw into the solution until the conductivity is minimal. Record your observations and conclusions. Balance the equation for the reaction, and write the total ionic and net ionic equations.

C. Net Ionic Equations—A Study Assignment

Balance the following neutralization reactions; write the total ionic and net ionic equations. Refer to *Writing Net Ionic Equations* for directions and examples.

1. Strong Acid and Strong Base:

$$HCl(aq) \ + \ NaOH(aq) \ \rightarrow \ NaCl(aq) \ + \ H_2O(l)$$

2. Strong Acid and Weak Base:

$$HCl(aq) \ + \ NH_4OH(aq) \ \rightarrow \ NH_4Cl(aq) \ + \ H_2O(l)$$

3. Weak Acid and Strong Base:

$$HF(aq) \ + \ NaOH(aq) \ \rightarrow \ NaF(aq) \ + \ H_2O(l)$$

4. Weak Acid and Weak Base:

$$HF(aq) \ + \ NH_4OH(aq) \ \rightarrow \ NH_4F(aq) \ + \ H_2O(l)$$

EXPERIMENT

NAME _____

DATE _____

SECTION _____

PRELABORATORY ASSIGNMENT*

1. Provide the key term that corresponds to each of the following definitions.

_____ (a) an aqueous solution that is a good conductor of electricity and produces a bright glow from a light bulb in a conductivity apparatus

_____ (b) an aqueous solution that is a poor conductor of electricity and produces a dim glow from a light bulb in a conductivity apparatus

_____ (c) the process of an ionic compound dissolving in water and separating into positive and negative ions

_____ (d) the process of a polar molecular compound dissolving in water and forming positive and negative ions

_____ (e) a chemical equation that portrays highly ionized substances in the ionic form and slightly ionized substances in the nonionized form

_____ (f) ions in aqueous solution that do not participate in a reaction, and do not appear in the net ionic equation

_____ (g) a chemical equation that portrays an ionic reaction after spectator ions have been canceled from the total ionic equation

Key Terms: dissociation, ionization, net ionic equation, spectator ions, strong electrolyte, total ionic equation, weak electrolyte

2. What is observed when conductivity testing the following:

(a) strong electrolyte

(b) weak electrolyte

3. Refer to Table 1 and indicate whether the following are strong or weak electrolytes.

(a) $HCl(aq)$ (b) $HC_2H_3O_2(aq)$

(c) $NaOH(aq)$ (d) $NH_4OH(aq)$

(e) $NaCl(aq)$ (f) $AgCl(s)$

---

* Answers at the end of the experiment.

4. Distinguish between NaCl(s) and NaCl(aq).

5. Given the following observations, write each of the following as it exists in aqueous solution.

   (a) HI(aq) — strong electrolyte

   (b) HF(aq) — weak electrolyte

   (c) $Sr(OH)_2$(aq) — strong electrolyte

   (d) $AgNO_3$(aq) — strong electrolyte

   (e) Ag_2SO_4(s) — weak electrolyte

6. Why must the electrodes on the conductivity apparatus, as well as all beakers, be rinsed with *distilled* water before each conductivity test?

7. What safety precautions should be observed in this experiment?

EXPERIMENT

DATE _____

NAME _____

SECTION _____

DATA TABLE

A. Conductivity Testing—Evidence for Ions in Aqueous Solution

Solution	Observation	Conclusion	Ionized/Nonionized
LiOH (aq)	bulb glows brightly	strong electrolyte	$Li^+(aq)$ + $OH^-(aq)$
HNO_2(aq)	bulb glows dimly	weak electrolyte	HNO_2(aq)
1. H_2O – distilled H_2O – tap			– omit –
2. NaCl (s) NaCl (aq)			
3. $CaCO_3$(s) $CaCO_3$(aq)			
4. $CaCl_2$(s) $CaCl_2$(aq)			

RECYCLE
Chemical
Waste

Solution	Observation	Conclusion	Ionized/Nonionized
5. (a) HCl(aq)			
(b) HC$_2$H$_3$O$_2$(aq)			
(c) HNO$_3$(aq)			
(d) NaOH (aq)			
(e) NH$_4$OH(aq)			
(f) KI (aq)			
(g) Al(NO$_3$)$_3$(aq)			
(h) Mg(OH)$_2$(aq)			
(i) CuSO$_4$(aq)			
(j) Ca(NO$_3$)$_2$(aq)			

RECYCLE
Chemical
Waste

B. Conductivity Testing—Evidence for a Chemical Reaction

Solution	Observation	Conclusion

1. (a) $HC_2H_3O_2(aq)$ _____ _____

   (b) $NH_4OH(aq)$ _____ _____

   (c) $HC_2H_3O_2(aq)$ + $NH_4OH(aq)$ _____ _____

equation: $HC_2H_3O_2(aq)$ + $NH_4OH(aq)$ → $NH_4C_2H_3O_2(aq)$ + $H_2O(l)$

total ionic:

net ionic:

2. (a) $H_2SO_4(aq)$ _____ _____

   (b) $Ba(OH)_2(aq)$ _____ _____

   (c) $H_2SO_4(aq)$ + $Ba(OH)_2(aq)$ _____ _____

equation: $H_2SO_4(aq)$ + $Ba(OH)_2(aq)$ → $BaSO_4(s)$ + $H_2O(l)$

total ionic:

net ionic:

RECYCLE
Chemical
Waste

3. (a) $Ba(OH)_2(aq)$ — see 2. (b) above _____ _____

   (b) $CO_2(g)$ _____ _____

   (c) $Ba(OH)_2(aq)$ + $CO_2(g)$ _____ _____

equation: $Ba(OH)_2(aq)$ + $CO_2(g)$ → $BaCO_3(s)$ + $H_2O(l)$

total ionic:

net ionic:

C. Net Ionic Equations—A Study Assignment

   1. Strong Acid and Strong Base:

equation: $HCl(aq)$ + $NaOH(aq)$ $\rightarrow$ $NaCl(aq)$ + $H_2O(l)$

total ionic:

net ionic:

_____

   2. Strong Acid and Weak Base:

equation: $HCl(aq)$ + $NH_4OH(aq$ $\rightarrow$ $NH_4Cl(aq)$ + $H_2O(l)$

total ionic:

net ionic:

_____

   3. Weak Acid and Strong Base:

equation: $HF(aq)$ + $NaOH(aq)$ $\rightarrow$ $NaF(aq)$ + $H_2O(l)$

total ionic:

net ionic:

_____

   4. Weak Acid and Weak Base:

equation: $HF(aq)$ + $NH_4OH(aq$ $\rightarrow$ $NH_4F(aq)$ + $H_2O(l)$

total ionic:

net ionic:

_____

EXPERIMENT

DATE _____

NAME _____

SECTION _____

POSTLABORATORY ASSIGNMENT

1. Why is distilled water a weaker conductor than tap water? (Refer to **A.1** in the Data Table.)

_____

2. Why is solid sodium chloride a weak electrolyte, while aqueous NaCl is a strong electrolyte? (Refer to **A.2** in the Data Table.)

_____

3. Why is calcium carbonate a weak electrolyte, while calcium chloride is a strong electrolyte? (Refer to **A.3** and **A.4** in the Data Table.)

_____

4. Why are aqueous solutions of $HC_2H_3O_2$ and NH_4OH weak electrolytes individually, but a strong electrolyte after they are added together? (Refer to **B.1** in the Data Table.)

_____

5. Why are aqueous solutions of H_2SO_4 and $Ba(OH)_2$ strong electrolytes individually, but a weak electrolyte after they are added together? (Refer to **B.2** in the Data Table.)

_____

6. Why does blowing carbon dioxide gas into aqueous barium hydroxide, $Ba(OH)_2$, reduce the conductivity from a strong electrolyte to a weak electrolyte? (Refer to **B.3** in the Data Table.)

_____

7. Balance the following precipitation reactions; write the total ionic and net ionic equations.

(a) $CuCl_2(aq)$ + $K_2CO_3(aq)$ $\rightarrow$ $CuCO_3(s)$ + $KCl(aq)$

total ionic:

net ionic:

(b) $CuCl_2(aq)$ + $Na_2S(aq)$ $\rightarrow$ $CuS(s)$ + $NaCl(aq)$

total ionic:

net ionic:

(c) $CuCl_2(aq)$ + $NH_4OH(aq)$ $\rightarrow$ $Cu(OH)_2(s)$ + $NH_4Cl(aq)$

total ionic:

net ionic:

8. (optional) Write a balanced chemical equation for the addition of aqueous calcium chloride and lithium nitrate solutions. Show the total ionic and net ionic equations.

ANSWERS TO PRELABORATORY ASSIGNMENTS

1. See the Glossary.
2. (a) the light bulb glows brightly; (b) the light bulb glows dimly
3. (a) strong electrolyte; (b) weak electrolyte; (c) strong electrolyte; (d) weak electrolyte; (e) strong electrolyte; (f) weak electrolyte
4. $NaCl(s)$ is a solid salt, and $NaCl(aq)$ is the salt dissolved in aqueous solution.
5. (a) ionized $H^+(aq)$ + $I^-(aq)$; (b) nonionized $HF(aq)$; (c) ionized $Sr^{2+}(aq)$ and $2\ OH^-(aq)$; (d) ionized $Ag^+(aq)$ and $NO_3^-(aq)$; (e) nonionized $Ag_2SO_4(s)$
6. The electrodes and beakers must be rinsed with distilled water to avoid a false-positive conductivity test for a weak electrolyte.
7. • Wear safety goggles; be careful to avoid contact with the chemical solutions.
   • Do not touch the exposed wire electrodes, as the wires can give a serious shock.
   • Dispose of chemical waste in the designated container.

Analysis of Vinegar

- To prepare a standard sodium hydroxide solution.
- To determine the molar concentration and mass/mass percent concentration of acetic acid in an unknown vinegar solution.
- To gain proficiency in the laboratory technique of titration.

DISCUSSION

In this experiment, we will neutralize an acidic solution of vinegar using a basic solution of sodium hydroxide. We determine the amount of sodium hydroxide necessary by performing a **titration** using a buret. When the acid is completely neutralized by the base, the titration stops. This is called the **endpoint** in the titration and is signaled when an **indicator** changes color. At the endpoint in the titration, a single drop of base is sufficient to bring about a permanent color change. Figure 1 illustrates a typical titration.

From Experiment 20 of *Laboratory Manual to Accompany Introductory Chemistry: Concepts and Critical Thinking*, Sixth Edition. Charles H. Corwin. Copyright © 2013 by Pearson Education, Inc. All rights reserved.

Preparation of a Standard Sodium Hydroxide Solution

We begin by diluting 6 *M* NaOH with water. Since diluting NaOH provides only an approximate concentration and it is necessary to know the concentration of NaOH precisely, we will prepare a **standard solution** by titration.

First, we weigh crystals of potassium hydrogen phthalate, $KHC_8H_4O_4$ (abbreviated KHP). After dissolving the KHP crystals in water, we will titrate the acid solution with NaOH according to the following equation.

$$KHP(aq) + NaOH(aq) \rightarrow KNaP(aq) + H_2O(l)$$

Example Exercise 1 • Molar Concentration of Standard NaOH

A 0.515 g sample of KHP (204.23 g/mol) is dissolved in water and requires 12.75 mL of NaOH solution to reach a faint pink endpoint. Find the molarity of the NaOH solution.

Solution: Referring to the preceding equation for the reaction and applying the rules of stoichiometry, we have

$$0.515 \text{ g KHP} \times \frac{1 \text{ mol KHP}}{204.23 \text{ g KHP}} \times \frac{1 \text{ mol NaOH}}{1 \text{ mol KHP}} = 0.00252 \text{ mol NaOH}$$

The molarity of the NaOH is found as follows:

$$\frac{0.00252 \text{ mol NaOH}}{12.75 \text{ mL solution}} \times \frac{1000 \text{ mL}}{1 \text{ L}} = \frac{0.198 \text{ mol NaOH}}{1 \text{ L solution}} = 0.198 \text{ } M \text{ NaOH}$$

In this example, the concentration of the standard NaOH solution is 0.198 *M*.

Titration of Acetic Acid in a Vinegar Unknown

After preparing a standard NaOH solution, we will determine the concentration of acetic acid in an unknown vinegar solution. A sample of vinegar will be titrated with NaOH to a permanent endpoint. The equation for the reaction is

$$HC_2H_3O_2(aq) \ + \ NaOH(aq) \ \rightarrow \ NaC_2H_3O_2(aq) \ + \ H_2O(l)$$

The following example exercise illustrates the calculation for the percentage of acetic acid in an unknown vinegar sample.

Example Exercise 2 • Percentage of Acetic Acid in Vinegar

The titration of a 10.0-mL vinegar sample requires 38.05 mL of standard 0.198 M NaOH. Calculate the (a) molarity and (b) mass/mass percent concentration of acetic acid.

Solution: We can calculate the moles of acetic acid from the moles of NaOH solution:

$$38.05 \ \cancel{\text{mL solution}} \ \times \ \frac{0.198 \ \cancel{\text{mol NaOH}}}{1000 \ \cancel{\text{mL solution}}} \ \times \ \frac{1 \ \text{mol HC}_2\text{H}_3\text{O}_2}{1 \ \cancel{\text{mol NaOH}}} \ = \ 0.00753 \ \text{mol HC}_2\text{H}_3\text{O}_2$$

(a) The molar concentration of $HC_2H_3O_2$ is

$$\frac{0.00753 \ \text{mol HC}_2\text{H}_3\text{O}_2}{10.0 \ \cancel{\text{mL}} \ \text{solution}} \ \times \ \frac{1000 \ \cancel{\text{mL}}}{1 \ \text{L}} \ = \ \frac{0.753 \ \text{mol HC}_2\text{H}_3\text{O}_2}{1 \ \text{L solution}}$$

$$= \ 0.753 \ M \ \text{HC}_2\text{H}_3\text{O}_2$$

(b) To calculate the m/m % concentration, we must know the density of the vinegar (1.01 g/mL) and the molar mass of acetic acid (60.06 g/mol).

$$\frac{0.753 \ \cancel{\text{mol HC}_2\text{H}_3\text{O}_2}}{1000 \ \cancel{\text{mL solution}}} \ \times \ \frac{60.06 \ \text{g HC}_2\text{H}_3\text{O}_2}{1 \ \cancel{\text{mol HC}_2\text{H}_3\text{O}_2}} \ \times \ \frac{1 \ \cancel{\text{mL solution}}}{1.01 \ \text{g solution}} \ \times \ 100\%$$

$$= \ 4.48\% \ \text{HC}_2\text{H}_3\text{O}_2$$

EQUIPMENT and CHEMICALS

- buret stand & clamp
- ring stand & utility clamp (optional)
- 50-mL buret
- small, plastic funnel (optional)
- 150-mL beaker
- graduated cylinder
- 1000-mL Florence flask w/stopper
- 125-mL Erlenmeyer flasks (3)
- 10-mL pipet & bulb
- 100-mL beaker
- wash bottle with distilled water

- dilute sodium hydroxide, 6 M NaOH
- potassium hydrogen phthalate, solid KHC$_8$H$_4$O$_4$ (KHP)
- phenolphthalein indicator (or, cresol red indicator)
- unknown vinegar solution, 3.00–5.00% HC$_2$H$_3$O$_2$

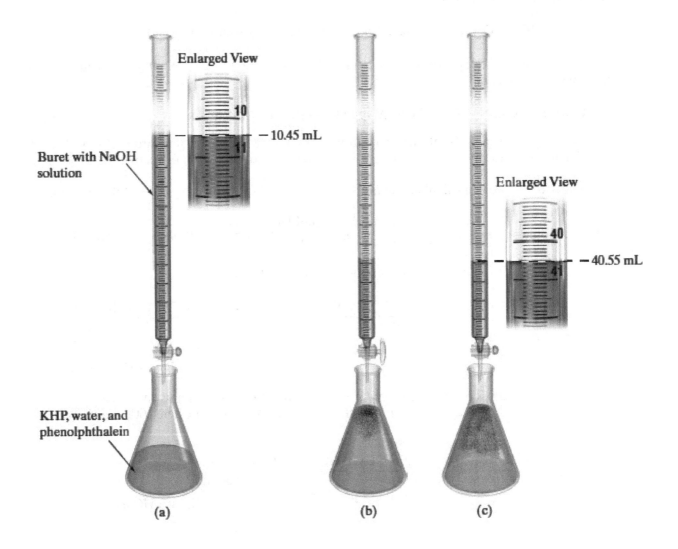

Figure 1 Apparatus for Titrating an Acid with a Base
(a) Read the initial volume of NaOH in the buret (10.45 mL). (b) A flash of
color indicates nearing the endpoint. (c) A permanent color signals the endpoint
for the titration (40.55 mL). In the example shown, the volume of NaOH is
40.55 mL – 10.45 mL = 30.10 mL.

PROCEDURE

A. Preparation of Sodium Hydroxide Solution

1. Half-fill a 1000-mL Florence flask with ~500 mL of distilled water. Measure ~15 mL of 6 M NaOH into a graduated cylinder and pour the NaOH into the Florence flask. Stopper the flask, and carefully swirl to mix the solution.

2. Condition a buret with NaOH solution from the Florence flask. Use a small funnel and half-fill the buret with NaOH. Allow some solution to pass through the buret tip into a 150-mL beaker, and empty the remainder into the sink.

3. Close the stopcock, and fill the buret with NaOH solution from the Florence flask.

   Note: Carefully add NaOH solution to the funnel so as to not overfill the buret.

4. Label the 125-mL Erlenmeyer flasks #1, #2, and #3. Precisely weigh ~0.5 g of KHP into each of the flasks. Add ~25 mL of distilled water to each flask, and heat as necessary to dissolve the KHP crystals.

   Note: If a digital electronic balance is available, the Instructor may direct students to tare weigh the KHP samples.

5. Titrate three KHP samples as follows:
   - Drain NaOH through the tip of the buret to clear any air bubbles.
   - Position Erlenmeyer flask #1 under the buret as shown in Figure 1.
   - Record the initial buret reading (± 0.05 mL).
   - Add a drop of indicator to the flask.
   - Titrate with NaOH to a permanent endpoint while slowly swirling the flask.
   - Record the final buret reading (± 0.05 mL).

6. Refill the buret with NaOH solution, record the initial buret reading, add a drop of indicator to flask #2, titrate the KHP sample, and record the final buret reading.

7. Refill the buret with NaOH solution, record the initial buret reading, add a drop of indicator to flask #3, titrate the KHP sample, and record the final buret reading.

RECYCLE
Chemical
Waste

8. Calculate the molarity of the NaOH solution for each trial. Record the average molarity of NaOH in the Data Table of Procedure B.

Note: *Save the NaOH in the Florence flask for Procedure B.*

B. Titration of Acetic Acid in Vinegar

1. Obtain ~50 mL of vinegar solution in a dry 100-mL beaker. Record the unknown number in the Data Table.

2. Condition a pipet with unknown vinegar solution, and transfer a 10.0-mL sample into each 125-mL flask. Add ~25 mL of distilled water into each flask.

   Note: It is not necessary to use dry flasks.

3. Titrate three vinegar samples as follows:
   - Position Erlenmeyer flask #1 under the buret.
   - Record the initial buret reading (± 0.05 mL).
   - Add a drop of indicator to the flask.
   - Titrate with NaOH to a permanent endpoint while slowly swirling the flask.
   - Record the final buret reading (± 0.05 mL).

4. Refill the buret with NaOH solution, record the initial buret reading, add a drop of indicator to flask #2, titrate the vinegar sample, and record the final buret reading.

5. Refill the buret with NaOH solution, record the initial buret reading, add a drop of indicator to flask #3, titrate the vinegar sample, and record the final buret reading.

6. Calculate the molarity of acetic acid, $HC_2H_3O_2$, in the unknown vinegar solution.

7. Convert the molarity of $HC_2H_3O_2$ (60.06 g/mol) to mass/mass percent concentration. Assume the density is 1.01 g/mL for the unknown vinegar solution.

RECYCLE
Chemical
Waste

Note: ***When the titrations are complete, rinse the buret and glassware with distilled water to remove all traces of NaOH solution.***

EXPERIMENT _____   NAME _____

DATE _____   SECTION _____

PRELABORATORY ASSIGNMENT*

1. Provide the key term that corresponds to each of the following definitions.

    _____ (a) a procedure for obtaining the mass of a sample directly by first placing a container on an electronic balance and setting the balance to zero; second, add a sample to the container and record the mass of sample directly

    _____ (b) a procedure for delivering a measured volume of solution using a buret

    _____ (c) the clear lens at the surface of a liquid inside a buret

    _____ (d) to rinse a pipet or buret with a sample liquid to avoid dilution by water on the inside surface

    _____ (e) a substance that undergoes a color change according to the pH of a solution

    _____ (f) the stage in a titration when the indicator changes color

    _____ (g) a solution whose concentration has been established precisely

    _____ (h) an expression that relates the moles of solute dissolved in each liter of solution

    _____ (i) an expression that relates the mass of solute dissolved in 100 grams of solution

    Key Terms: condition, endpoint, indicator, m/m % concentration, meniscus, molar concentration, standard solution, tare weighing, titration

2. Observe and record the following buret readings.

    (a)

    (b)

3. How can you tell that you are nearing the endpoint in a titration?

4. What volume of NaOH is required to permanently change the indicator at the endpoint?

---

* Answers at the end of the experiment.

5. If KHP sample #1 requires 19.90 mL of NaOH solution to reach an endpoint, what volume should be required for samples #2 and #3?

6. If vinegar sample #1 requires 29.05 mL of NaOH solution to reach an endpoint, what volume should be required for samples #2 and #3?

7. A 0.875-g sample of KHP (204.23 g/mol) is dissolved in water and titrated with 20.75 mL of NaOH solution to a permanent endpoint. Refer to Example Exercise 1 and calculate the molarity of the NaOH solution.

8. A 10.0-mL vinegar sample is pipetted into an Erlenmeyer flask and titrated with 28.85 mL of 0.206 M NaOH to a permanent endpoint.

    (a) Refer to Example Exercise 2 and calculate the molarity of the acetic acid in the vinegar.

    (b) Assume the density of the vinegar solution is 1.01 g/mL and find the mass/mass percent concentration of acetic acid, $HC_2H_3O_2$ (60.06 g/mol), in the unknown vinegar sample.

9. Which of the following is a serious source of experimental error?
    (a) The Erlenmeyer flasks are not dry before weighing the KHP samples.
    (b) The KHP samples are dissolved in 50 mL (*not 25 mL*) of distilled water.
    (c) The sodium hydroxide is not mixed completely in the Florence flask.
    (d) The buret is not conditioned.
    (e) Bubbles are not cleared from the tip of the buret.
    (f) Two drops (*not one drop*) of indicator is used.
    (g) Disposing of the standard NaOH solution before titrating the vinegar samples.
    (h) The Erlenmeyer flasks are not dry before pipetting the vinegar samples.

10. What safety precautions should be observed in this experiment?

EXPERIMENT _____ NAME _____

DATE _____ SECTION _____

DATA TABLE

A. Preparation of Sodium Hydroxide Solution

mass of Erlenmeyer flask + KHP _____ g _____ g _____ g

mass of Erlenmeyer flask _____ g _____ g _____ g

mass of KHP _____ g _____ g _____ g

final buret reading _____ mL _____ mL _____ mL

initial buret reading _____ mL _____ mL _____ mL

volume of NaOH _____ mL _____ mL _____ mL

Show the calculation of molarity of NaOH for trial 1 (see Example Exercise 1).

RECYCLE
Chemical
Waste

Molarity of NaOH _____ M _____ M _____ M

Average molarity of NaOH _____ M

B. Titration of Acetic Acid in Vinegar   **UNKNOWN #** _____

      Average molarity of NaOH (see Procedure A)   _____ *M*

      volume of vinegar   _____ mL _____ mL _____ mL

      final buret reading   _____ mL _____ mL _____ mL

      initial buret reading   _____ mL _____ mL _____ mL

      volume of NaOH   _____ mL _____ mL _____ mL

Show the calculation for the molarity of acetic acid for trial 1 (see Example Exercise 2).

RECYCLE
Chemical
Waste

      Molarity of $HC_2H_3O_2$ _____ *M* _____ *M* _____ *M*

      Average molarity of $HC_2H_3O_2$ _____ *M*

Show the calculation for the percent concentration of acetic acid for trial 1. (Assume the density of the vinegar solution is 1.01 g/mL.)

      Mass/mass percent $HC_2H_3O_2$ _____ % _____ % _____ %

      Average mass/mass percent $HC_2H_3O_2$ _____ %

EXPERIMENT   NAME   _____

DATE _____   SECTION _____

POSTLABORATORY ASSIGNMENT

1. A standard nitric acid solution is prepared using 0.425 g of sodium carbonate, Na_2CO_3. Find the molarity of the acid if 33.25 mL are required to reach a permanent endpoint.

    $$2\ HNO_3\ (aq)\quad +\quad Na_2CO_3\ (s)\quad \rightarrow\quad 2\ NaNO_3\ (aq)\quad +\quad H_2O(l)\quad +\quad CO_2\ (g)$$

    _____

2. A 10.0-mL sample of household ammonia solution required 27.50 mL of 0.241 M HNO_3 for neutralization. Calculate (a) the molar concentration of the ammonia and (b) the mass/mass percent concentration of ammonia (17.04 g/mol), given a solution density of 0.985 g/mL.

    $$HNO_3\ (aq)\quad +\quad NH_3\ (aq)\quad \rightarrow\quad NH_4NO_3\ (aq)$$

    (a)_____

    (b)_____

3. A 10.0 mL sample of calcium hydroxide solution required 26.85 mL of 0.225 M hydrochloric acid for neutralization. Calculate (a) the molar concentration of the base.

    $$2\ HCl(aq)\quad +\quad Ca(OH)_2\ (aq)\quad \rightarrow\quad CaCl_2(aq)\quad +\quad 2\ H_2O(l)$$

    _____

4. A Rolaids tablet contains calcium carbonate for neutralizing stomach acid. If a Rolaids tablet neutralizes 24.65 mL of 0.547 M hydrochloric acid, how many milligrams of calcium carbonate are in a Rolaids tablet?

$$CaCO_3(s) \ + \ 2\,HCl\,(aq) \ \rightarrow \ CaCl_2\,(aq) \ + \ H_2O(l) \ + \ CO_2(g)$$

_____

5. (optional) A student diluted 15.0 mL of 6 M NaOH solution into 485.0 mL of distilled water. Calculate the molarity of the diluted base solution.

_____

Explain why this diluted NaOH solution *cannot* be used as a standard solution.

ANSWERS TO PRELABORATORY ASSIGNMENTS

1. See the Glossary.
2. (a) 0.50 mL   (b) 31.35 mL
3. You are nearing the endpoint in a titration when flashes of indicator color persist longer.
4. Only 1 drop of NaOH is required to change the indicator permanently at the endpoint.
5. The volume of NaOH required for an endpoint varies for each trial, depending on the mass of the KHP sample.
6. The volume of NaOH required for an endpoint should be about the same for each trial because the amount of acetic acid is the same in each vinegar sample.
7. 0.206 M NaOH
8. (a) 0.594 M $HC_2H_3O_2$; (b) 3.53% $HC_2H_3O_2$
9. (c), (d), (e), and (g) are serious errors.
10. • Wear safety goggles; be careful when using the laboratory burner, pipet, and buret.
    • Add NaOH carefully to the buret through the funnel, and avoid overfilling with NaOH.
    • Avoid contact with NaOH. In the event of contact, wash the area immediately with water and notify the Instructor.
    • Dispose of chemical waste in the designated container.

Families of Elements

OBJECTIVES

- To study similar chemical properties for groups of elements in the periodic table.
- To observe flame tests and reactions for barium, calcium, lithium, potassium, sodium, and strontium solutions.
- To observe halide tests for bromide, chloride, and iodide solutions.
- To identify the alkali or alkaline earth element and the halide in an unknown solution.

DISCUSSION

In 1869, the Russian chemist Dmitri Mendeleev proposed that elements in the periodic table should be arranged by increasing atomic mass. In 1913, the English physicist Harry Moseley found that the elements should actually be arranged according to increasing atomic number. The modern **periodic law** states that the properties of elements in the periodic table recur in a repeating pattern, when the elements are arranged according to *increasing atomic number*.

The elements in the periodic table are found in rows and columns. Elements in horizontal rows are called **periods**, or series. The elements in vertical columns are called **groups**, or families. Within each group of elements there are similarities in chemical properties. In this experiment, we will study three families of elements, the **alkali metals**, **alkaline earth metals**, and **halides**. We can identify the elements that belong to the same family by their similar chemical reactions.

In this experiment we will observe flame tests and solution reactions for alkali and alkaline earth elements. A **flame test** is performed by placing a small amount of solution on the coiled end of a wire. The wire is then held in a burner flame, and the flame color is observed (see Figure 1). For example, an orange-yellow flame shows the presence of sodium in solution.

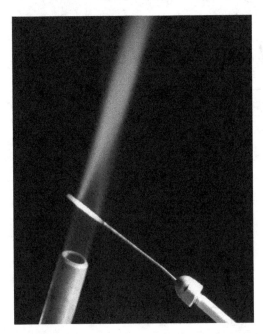

Figure 1 Flame-Test Technique A wire with a drop of solution in the coiled tip is placed in a hot burner flame. The color of the flame indicates the presence of a given element; a brief, yellow-green flame indicates the presence of barium; a brick-red flame indicates calcium; a scarlet-red flame indicates lithium; a violet flame indicates potassium; and a bright red flame indicates strontium.

Although the colors are specific for each element, flame tests can be misleading. Sodium is usually present as an impurity, and gives a weak yellow flame test. The intensity of the yellow flame for a sodium impurity is not as strong, and the distinction between a sodium impurity and a sodium sample can be made with a little practice.

EQUIPMENT and CHEMICALS

- 13 x 100 mm test tubes (6) & test tube rack
- test tube brush
- flame-test wire (nichrome or platinum wire)
- wash bottle with distilled water

- ammonium carbonate solution 0.5 M $(NH_4)_2CO_3$
- ammonium phosphate solution 0.5 M $(NH_4)_2HPO_4$
- ammonium sulfate solution 0.5 M $(NH_4)_2SO_4$

- barium solution, 0.5 M $BaCl_2$
- calcium solution, 0.5 M $CaCl_2$
- lithium solution, 0.5 M LiCl
- potassium solution, 0.5 M KCl
- sodium solution, 0.5 M NaCl
- strontium solution, 0.5 M $SrCl_2$
- bromide solution, 0.5 M NaBr
- chloride solution, 0.5 M NaCl
- iodide solution, 0.1 M NaI
- hexane, C_6H_{14}
- dilute nitric acid, 6 M HNO_3
- chlorine water (bleach)
- unknown solutions

PROCEDURE

A. Analysis of Known Solutions

1. *Flame Tests of Known Solutions*

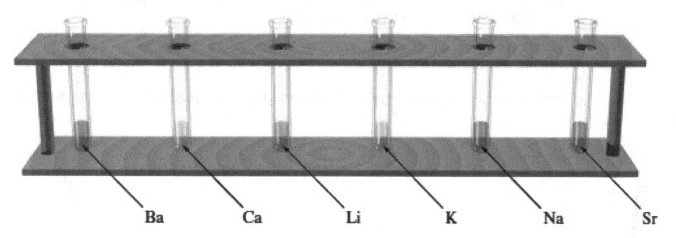

Figure 2 Alkali and Alkaline Earth Tests Solutions of barium, calcium, lithium, potassium, sodium, and strontium are placed in separate test tubes.

(b) Obtain a flame-test wire and make a small loop in the end. Remove contamination by placing the wire loop at the tip of a burner flame. Continue to heat the wire until there is no longer any color produced in the flame.

Note: If a flame-test wire continues to produce a colored flame, dip the wire into dilute hydrochloric acid and heat the wire until red hot.

RECYCLE
Chemical
Waste

(c) Dip the clean flame-test wire into the test tube containing barium solution. Place the wire loop at the tip of the flame (see Figure 1). Record your observation. Clean the wire and repeat the flame test for calcium, lithium, potassium, sodium, and strontium solutions.

2. *Reactions of Known Solutions*

(a) Add a few drops of ammonium carbonate, $(NH_4)_2CO_3$, solution in each test tube that was used for the flame test. If a precipitate forms, record *ppt* in the Data Table. If there is no reaction, record *NR*.

(b) Clean the test tubes and rinse with distilled water. Put 10 drops of the barium, calcium, lithium, potassium, sodium, and strontium solutions into separate test tubes. Add a few drops of ammonium phosphate, $(NH_4)_3PO_4$, solution in each test tube. Record your observations in the Data Table.

(c) Clean the test tubes and put 10 drops of barium, calcium, lithium, potassium, sodium, and strontium solutions in separate test tubes. Add a few drops of ammonium sulfate, $(NH_4)_2SO_4$, in each test tube and record your observations.

3. *Halide Tests of Known Solutions*

(a) Place three test tubes in a test tube rack. Add 10 drops of bromide solution, chloride solution, and iodide solution into separate test tubes.

(b) Add 10 drops of hexane, C_6H_{14}, 1 drop of nitric acid, HNO_3, and 5 drops of chlorine water to each test tube (Figure 3).

(c) Shake each test tube and observe the color of the upper hexane layer.

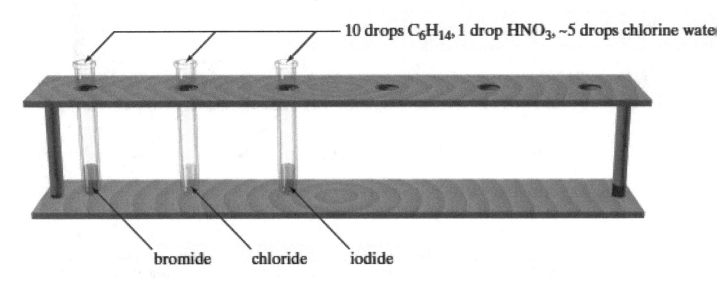

10 drops C_6H_{14}, 1 drop HNO_3, ~5 drops chlorine water

bromide   chloride   iodide

Figure 3 Halide Tests Hexane, nitric acid, and chlorine water are added to 10 drops of bromide, chloride, and iodide solutions in separate test tubes.

RECYCLE
Chemical
Waste

Note: The color of the upper hexane layer confirms the presence of bromide, chloride, or iodide. An orange color indicates bromide; a clear color indicates chloride; and a purple color indicates iodide.

Note: Dispose of the hexane layer in the organic waste container.

B. Analysis of an Unknown Solution

1. *Flame Test* Record the unknown number of a solution assigned by the Instructor. Perform a flame test on the solution, and record your observation in the Data Table.

2. *Solution Reactions* Put 10 drops of unknown solution into three test tubes. Add a few drops of ammonium carbonate, $(NH_4)_2CO_3$, to the first test tube; a few drops of ammonium phosphate, $(NH_4)_3PO_4$, to the second; and a few drops of ammonium sulfate, $(NH_4)_2SO_4$, to the third. Record your observations in the Data Table.

3. *Halide Test* Put 10 drops of unknown solution into a test tube. Add 10 drops of hexane, C_6H_{14}, 1 drop of nitric acid, HNO_3, and 5 drops of chlorine water. Shake the test tube and record the color of the upper hexane layer.

EXPERIMENT   NAME   _____

DATE   _____   SECTION   _____

PRELABORATORY ASSIGNMENT*

1. Provide the key term that corresponds to each of the following definitions.

    _____ (a)   the properties of the elements recur in a repeating pattern when arranged according to increasing atomic number

    _____ (b)   a horizontal row of elements in the periodic table

    _____ (c)   a vertical column of elements in the periodic table having similar properties

    _____ (d)   any Group IA/1 element in the periodic table, excluding hydrogen

    _____ (e)   any Group IIA/2 element in the periodic table

    _____ (f)   a negatively charged Group VIIA/17 atom; e.g., bromide, chloride, iodide

    _____ (h)   a means of identifying an element by observing the characteristic color it emits when placed in a hot flame

    _____ (h)   an insoluble solid substance produced from a reaction in aqueous solution

    _____ (i)   refers to liquids that do not dissolve in one another and separate into two layers

    Key Terms: alkali metal, alkaline earth metal, flame test, group, halide, immiscible, period, periodic law, precipitate (ppt)

2. Which three alkali elements are investigated in this experiment?

    Which three alkaline earth elements are investigated in this experiment?

3. Refer to **Figure 1** to answer the following.

    (a)   Which element is indicated by a brief *yellow-green* flame test?   _____

    (b)   Which element is indicated by a *brick-red* flame test?   _____

    (c)   Which element is indicated by a *scarlet-red* flame test?   _____

    (d)   Which element is indicated by a *violet* flame test?   _____

    (e)   Which element is indicated by a *strong yellow* flame test?   _____

    (f)   Which element is indicated by a *bright red* flame test?   _____

_____

* *Answers at the end of the experiment.*

4. Where is the end of the wire placed when performing a flame test?

5. Which element occurs as an impurity and gives a weak yellow flame test?

6. Which three halides are investigated in this experiment?

7. Is water and hexane *miscible* or *immiscible*?

8. Is the halide test observed in the *upper layer* or *lower layer*?

9. Refer to **Figure 3** to answer the following.

    (a) Which halide is indicated by an *orange* upper layer? _____

    (b) Which halide is indicated by a *clear* upper layer? _____

    (c) Which halide is indicated by a *purple* upper layer? _____

10. What safety precautions should be observed in this experiment?

Families of Elements

EXPERIMENT   NAME _____

DATE _____   SECTION _____

DATA TABLE

A. Analysis of Known Solutions

   1. *Flame Tests of Known Solutions*

Solution Tested	Flame Test Observations
barium solution	_____
calcium solution	_____
lithium solution	_____
potassium solution	_____
sodium solution	_____
strontium solution	_____

   2. *Reactions of Known Solutions*

Solution Tested	Solution Reaction Observations		
	ammonium carbonate	ammonium phosphate	ammonium sulfate
barium solution	_____	_____	_____
calcium solution	_____	_____	*
lithium solution	_____	_____	_____
potassium solution	_____	_____	_____
sodium solution	_____	_____	_____
strontium solution	_____	_____	_____

   * Heat gently if NR.

   3. *Halide Tests of Known Solutions*

Solution Tested	Hexane Layer Observations
bromide solution	_____
chloride solution	_____
iodide solution	_____

RECYCLE Chemical Waste

165

B. Analysis of an Unknown Solution   **UNKNOWN #** _____

1. *Flame Test of an Unknown Solution*

Solution Tested	Flame Test Observation
unknown solution	_____

2. *Reactions of an Unknown Solution*

	Solution Reaction Observations		
Solution Tested	ammonium carbonate	ammonium phosphate	ammonium sulfate
unknown solution	_____	_____	_____

Compare the flame test and solution reactions for the unknown to the observations in Procedures A.1 and A.2. Identify the alkali or the alkaline earth element present in the unknown solution; **circle** *one of the following.*

barium   calcium   lithium   potassium   sodium   strontium

3. *Halide Test of an Unknown Solution*

Solution Tested	Hexane Layer Observation
unknown solution	_____

Compare the hexane layer observation for the unknown solution to the observations in Procedure A.3. Identify the halide present in the unknown solution; **circle** *one of the following.*

bromide   chloride   iodide

RECYCLE
Chemical
Waste

EXPERIMENT   NAME _____

DATE _____   SECTION _____

POSTLABORATORY ASSIGNMENT

1. Refer to Data Table A.2 and state the solutions that produce reactions similar to:

   (a) Li   _____   (b) Ba   _____

2. State the elements in this experiment that belong to:

   (a) Group IA/1   _____   (b) Group IIA/2   _____

3. An unknown solution gives a brief green flame test. The unknown gives a white precipitate with ammonium carbonate, ammonium phosphate, and ammonium sulfate. The halide test produces a purple color in the upper hexane layer. Identify (a) the alkali or alkaline earth element, and (b) the halide present in the unknown solution.

   (a) _____   (b) _____

4. An unknown solution gives a scarlet-red flame test. The unknown gives no reaction with ammonium carbonate, ammonium phosphate, and ammonium sulfate. The halide test produces an orange color in the upper hexane layer. Identify (a) the alkali or alkaline earth element, and (b) the halide present in the unknown solution.

   (a) _____   (b) _____

5. An unknown solution gives a brick-red flame test with flashes of yellow. The unknown gives a white precipitate with ammonium carbonate and ammonium phosphate, but no reaction with ammonium sulfate. The halide test produces no reaction in the upper hexane layer. Identify (a) the alkali or alkaline earth element, and (b) the halide present in the unknown solution.

   (a) _____   (b) _____

6. Fireworks are produced by gunpowder and chemicals in a rocket shell that is fired into the air and exploded. Based on your experimental observations, which elements could produce the following colors of fireworks?

   (a) bright red   _____   (b) yellow   _____

7. In groups of elements, the metallic character (*increases / decreases*) up a group.
   In groups of elements, the atomic radius (*increases / decreases*) up a group.

8. In periods of elements, the metallic character (*increases / decreases*) left to right.
   In periods of elements, the atomic radius (*increases / decreases*) left to right.

9. Refer to the periodic table on the inside front cover of this lab manual. Select the symbol of the element that corresponds to the following description.

    (a)   the metal in Period 3, Group IA/1   _____

    (b)   the semimetal in Period 2, Group IIIA/13   _____

    (c)   the nonmetal in Period 1, Group VIIIA/18   _____

    (d)   the alkali metal in Period 4   _____

    (e)   the alkaline earth metal in Period 4   _____

    (f)   the halogen in Period 4   _____

    (g)   the noble gas in Period 4   _____

    (h)   the representative element in Period 4, Group IVA/14 _____

    (i)   the transition element in Period 4, Group IVB/4   _____

    (j)   the rare earth element in Period 4   _____

    (k)   the radioactive element in Period 5   _____

    (l)   the lowest atomic mass lanthanide   _____

    (m) the lowest atomic number actinide   _____

    (n)   the first transuranium element   _____

    (o)   the element with atomic mass 196.97 amu   _____

    (p)   the element with atomic number 80   _____

    (q)   the element with mass number 222   _____

    (r)   the representative element in Period 4 with three valence electrons _____

    (s)   the representative element in Period 4 with six valence electrons _____

    (t)   the nonmetal in Group IA/1   _____

10. (optional) Refer to the periodic table on the inside front cover of this lab manual. Which two elements in the fourth period violate the original periodic law as stated by Mendeleev?

ANSWERS TO PRELABORATORY ASSIGNMENTS

1. See the Glossary.
2. alkali: Li, K, Na; alkaline earth: Ba, Ca, Sr
3. (a) Ba; (b) Ca; (c) Li; (d) K; (e) Na; (f) Sr
4. When performing a flame test, the end of the wire is placed at the tip of the burner flame.
5. Sodium impurity gives a weak, yellow, flame test. An aqueous sodium solution gives a strong, long-lasting, flame test.
6. bromide, chloride, iodide
7. Water and hexane are *immiscible* and separate into two layers.
8. The halide test is observed in the *upper layer*.
9. (a) bromide; (b) chloride; (c) iodide
10. • Wear safety goggles; be careful when using the burner and performing a flame test.
    • Handle acids carefully, and avoid breathing the vapors of conc hydrochloric acid.
    • Dispose of chemical waste in the designated container.

Empirical Formulas of Compounds

- To determine the empirical formula for magnesium oxide.
- To determine the empirical formula for copper sulfide.
- To gain practical experience in developing techniques using a crucible.

DISCUSSION

During the late 1700s, chemists experimented with elements to see how they reacted to form compounds. In particular, they were interested in the reactions of metals as they combined with oxygen in the air. By measuring the mass of a metal before reaction and the mass of the metal oxide after reaction, chemists were able to determine the formulas of metal oxide compounds.

The simplest whole number ratio of atoms in a compound is referred to as the **empirical formula**. Mendeleev placed an element in a particular group in the periodic table based on the empirical formula of its oxide. For example, he placed magnesium, calcium, strontium, and barium in Group IIA/2 because they react with oxygen to give similar empirical formulas; that is, MgO, CaO, SrO, and BaO.

Since transition metals can combine with nonmetals in different ratios, we cannot always predict the empirical formulas of transition metal compounds. For example, iron can combine with oxygen to form either iron(II) oxide, FeO, or iron(III) oxide, Fe_2O_3. The following example exercises illustrate the calculation of empirical formulas.

From Experiment 12 of *Laboratory Manual to Accompany Introductory Chemistry: Concepts and Critical Thinking*, Sixth Edition. Charles H. Corwin. Copyright © 2013 by Pearson Education, Inc.

Example Exercise 1 • Determining an Empirical Formula

A 0.279-g sample of iron is heated and allowed to react with oxygen from the air. If the product has a mass of 0.400 g, what is the empirical formula of the iron oxide?

Solution: The empirical formula is experimentally determined from the moles of each reactant. The moles of iron are calculated as follows.

$$0.279 \text{ g Fe} \quad \times \quad \frac{1 \text{ mol Fe}}{55.85 \text{ g Fe}} \quad = \quad 0.00500 \text{ mol Fe}$$

The mass of oxygen that reacted is 0.400 g product – 0.279 g iron = 0.121 g. We can calculate the moles of oxygen as follows.

$$0.121 \text{ g O} \quad \times \quad \frac{1 \text{ mol O}}{16.00 \text{ g O}} \quad = \quad 0.00756 \text{ mol O}$$

The mole ratio of the elements in iron oxide is $Fe_{0.00500}O_{0.00756}$, and we can divide by 0.00500 to find the simplest whole number ratio.

$$Fe \frac{0.00500}{0.00500} \; O \frac{0.00756}{0.00500} \quad = \quad Fe_{1.00}O_{1.51}$$

If we double the mole ratio, we obtain $Fe_2O_{3.02}$. The slight deviation from a whole number ratio is due to experimental error. Thus, the empirical formula is Fe_2O_3, and we name the compound iron(III) oxide, or ferric oxide.

Example Exercise 2 • Determining an Empirical Formula

A 0.331-g sample of iron is placed in a crucible and covered with powdered sulfur. The crucible is heated until all the excess sulfur is driven off. If the product weighs 0.522 g, what is the empirical formula of the iron sulfide?

Solution: First, we can calculate the moles of iron in the product.

$$0.331 \text{ g Fe} \quad \times \quad \frac{1 \text{ mol Fe}}{55.85 \text{ g Fe}} \quad = \quad 0.00593 \text{ mol Fe}$$

The mass of sulfur that reacted is 0.522 g product – 0.331 g iron = 0.191 g. Second, we can calculate the moles of sulfur as follows.

$$0.191 \text{ g S} \quad \times \quad \frac{1 \text{ mol S}}{32.07 \text{ g S}} \quad = \quad 0.00596 \text{ mol S}$$

The mole ratio of the elements in iron sulfide is $Fe_{0.00592}S_{0.00596}$, and we divide by 0.00592 to find the simplest whole number ratio.

$$Fe \frac{0.00593}{0.00593} \; S \frac{0.00596}{0.00593} \quad = \quad Fe_{1.00}S_{1.01}$$

The slight deviation from a whole number ratio is due to experimental error. Thus, the empirical formula for the product is FeS, and we name the compound iron(II) sulfide, or ferrous sulfide.

In this experiment, you will ignite magnesium ribbon in a crucible and convert the metal to an oxide product. The second part of the experiment involves the conversion of copper to copper sulfide. Since copper can form either copper(I) sulfide or copper(II) sulfide, the empirical formula is unknown and cannot be predicted. Figure 1 illustrates the experimental equipment.

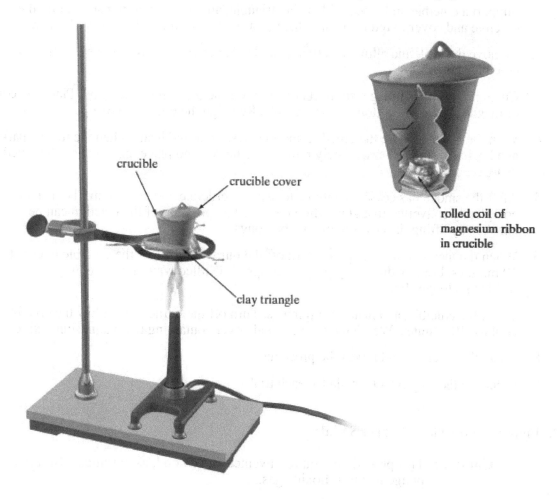

crucible

crucible cover

clay triangle

rolled coil of
magnesium ribbon
in crucible

Figure 1 Empirical Formula Apparatus A crucible and cover are placed in a
clay triangle on a ring stand, and heated until red hot.

EQUIPMENT and CHEMICALS

- crucible & cover
- clay triangle
- crucible tongs
- ring stand & ring

- magnesium, Mg ribbon
- copper, #18 gauge Cu wire
- sulfur, S powder

PROCEDURE

A. Empirical Formula of Magnesium Oxide

1. Support a crucible and cover with a clay triangle, and place on a ring stand. Fire the crucible and cover to red heat using the tip of the flame from a laboratory burner.

2. Remove the heat, and allow the crucible and cover to cool for 10 minutes. Weigh the crucible and cover.

3. Cut a 25-cm strip of magnesium ribbon, and roll the metal into a flat coil. Place the coil of magnesium at the bottom of the crucible. Reweigh the crucible, cover, and metal.

4. With the cover off, fire the crucible and magnesium to red heat. When the metal sparks and begins to smoke, immediately remove the burner and place the cover on the crucible using crucible tongs.

5. After the smoke has ceased, continue to heat the crucible and cover until the metal is completely converted to a gray-white residue. The progress of the reaction can be checked by lifting the cover with crucible tongs.

6. When the metal no longer sparks, turn off the burner and allow the crucible to cool for 10 minutes. Using a dropper pipet, add drops of distilled water until the gray-white residue no longer fizzes.

RECYCLE
Chemical
Waste

7. Cover the crucible, and heat for 5 minutes. Turn off the burner, and allow the crucible to cool for 10 minutes. Weigh the crucible and cover containing the magnesium oxide.

8. Clean the crucible, and repeat the procedure.

9. Calculate the empirical formula for each trial.

B. Empirical Formula of Copper Sulfide

Caution: This procedure requires a vented fume hood, as burning sulfur produces pungent sulfur dioxide gas.

1. Support a crucible and cover with a clay triangle, and place on a ring stand. Fire the crucible and cover to red heat.

2. Remove the heat, and allow the crucible and cover to cool for 10 minutes. Weigh the crucible and cover.

3. Cut a 25-cm length of copper wire, and roll the wire into a coil. Place the coil of wire in the bottom of the crucible. Reweigh the crucible, cover, and copper wire.

4. Cover the copper wire completely with powdered sulfur. Place the cover on the crucible, and gradually heat to red heat under a fume hood. Continue to heat for several minutes after the last trace of burning sulfur disappears.

5. Allow the crucible and contents to cool for 10 minutes. Weigh the crucible and cover containing the copper sulfide.

6. Clean the crucible, and repeat the procedure.

7. Calculate the empirical formula for each trial.

EXPERIMENT

NAME _____

DATE _____

SECTION _____

PRELABORATORY ASSIGNMENT*

1. Provide the key term that corresponds to each of the following definitions.

_____ (a) the chemical formula of a compound that expresses the simplest whole number ratio of atoms of each element in a molecule, or ions in a formula unit

_____ (b) the chemical formula of a compound that expresses the actual number of atoms of each element in a molecule

_____ (c) heating a crucible until it glows red

_____ (d) a repeated process of heating, cooling, and weighing until the mass readings for an object are constant, or agree closely

_____ (e) a procedure for obtaining the mass of a sample indirectly by first weighing a container and then weighing the container with the sample

_____ (f) the mass of 1 mole of any substance expressed in grams

_____ (g) the amount of substance that contains Avogadro's number of particles

Key Terms: empirical formula, firing to red heat, heating to constant weight, molar mass (MM), mole (mol), molecular formula, weighing by difference

2. Why are the empty crucible and cover fired to red heat?

3. How critical are the suggested times for heating and cooling?

4. Why is distilled water added to the crucible after igniting the magnesium metal?

5. How can you tell when the magnesium metal has reacted completely?

_____

* Answers at the end of the experiment.

6. How can you tell when the copper wire has reacted completely?

7. A sample of magnesium ribbon is ignited in a crucible to form magnesium oxide. Refer to Example Exercise 1 and determine the empirical formula of magnesium oxide from the following data:

mass of crucible and cover + magnesium metal	33.741 g
mass of crucible and cover	33.500 g
mass of crucible and cover + magnesium oxide	33.899 g

8. What are major sources of experimental error?

9. What safety precautions must be observed in this experiment?

EXPERIMENT   NAME   _____

DATE   _____   SECTION _____

DATA TABLE

A. Empirical Formula of Magnesium Oxide

mass of crucible and cover + magnesium metal   _____ g   _____ g
(before heating)

mass of crucible and cover   _____ g   _____ g

mass of magnesium metal   _____ g   _____ g

mass of crucible and cover + magnesium oxide
(after heating)   _____ g   _____ g

mass of combined oxygen   _____ g   _____ g
(after heating – before heating)

RECYCLE
Chemical
Waste

Show the calculation of the empirical formula for trial 1 (see Example Exercise 1).

Empirical formula of magnesium oxide   _____   _____

B. Empirical Formula of Copper Sulfide

mass of crucible and cover + copper wire
(before heating) _____ g _____ g

mass of crucible and cover _____ g _____ g

mass of copper wire _____ g _____ g

mass of crucible and cover + copper sulfide
(after heating) _____ g _____ g

mass of crucible and cover + copper sulfide
(optional second heating) _____ g _____ g

RECYCLE
Chemical
Waste

mass of combined sulfur
(after heating – before heating) _____ g _____ g

Show the calculation of the empirical formula for trial 1 (see Example Exercise 2).

Empirical formula of copper sulfide _____ _____

EXPERIMENT _____ NAME _____

DATE _____ SECTION _____

POSTLABORATORY ASSIGNMENT

1. Refer to the periodic table and predict the empirical formula for each of the following oxides given the formula of aluminum oxide, Al_2O_3.

    (a) $B_?O_?$ _____   (b) $Ga_?O_?$ _____

    (c) $In_?O_?$ _____   (d) $Tl_?O_?$ _____

2. Refer to the periodic table and predict the empirical formula for each of the following halides given the formula of magnesium chloride, $MgCl_2$.

    (a) magnesium fluoride _____   (b) calcium chloride _____

    (c) strontium bromide _____   (d) barium iodide _____

3. A 1.000-g sample of lead shot reacted with oxygen to give 1.077 g of product. Calculate the empirical formula of the lead oxide.

    _____

4. A 0.500-g sample of tin foil reacted with oxygen to give 0.635 g of product. Calculate the empirical formula of the tin oxide.

    _____

5. A 1.000-g sample of cobalt metal reacted with sulfur powder to give 1.544 g of product. Calculate the empirical formula of the cobalt sulfide.

_____

6. A 0.500-g sample of chromium metal reacted with sulfur powder to give 0.963 g of product. Calculate the empirical formula of the chromium sulfide.

_____

7. (optional) Mercury chloride is a commercial fungicide. If the molar mass is 470 g/mol and the percent composition is 85.0% Hg and 15.0% Cl, what is the empirical and molecular formula of the fungicide?

Empirical formula _____

Molecular formula _____

ANSWERS TO PRELABORATORY ASSIGNMENTS

1. See the Glossary.
2. The empty crucible and cover are fired to red heat to burn off impurities and establish a constant weight.
3. The suggested periods for heating and cooling are general guidelines.
4. Igniting magnesium in air produces magnesium oxide and magnesium nitride. Adding distilled water to the crucible decomposes magnesium nitride and releases ammonia gas. (The crucible contents fizz, and the odor of ammonia gas is noticeable.) Reheating the crucible and contents converts magnesium hydroxide to magnesium oxide.
5. If the magnesium has reacted completely, there are no sparks when lifting the crucible cover.
6. The copper wire has reacted completely when there is no longer traces of sulfur in the crucible. If there is any doubt, heat the crucible to constant weight.
7. $Mg_{0.00991}O_{0.00988} = MgO$
8. • A hot crucible on the balance causes a weighing error, and mass readings will be low.
   • If white smoke escapes from the crucible, the mass readings will be low.
   • Sulfur has a tendency to "creep" out of the crucible during the firing. The excess sulfur must be driven off by heating, or the mass readings will be high.
9. • Wear safety goggles; be careful when using the laboratory burner.
   • Carefully lift the crucible cover with tongs to check the progress of the reaction.
   • Before firing to red heat, set the crucible on the lab bench and strike sharply with a pencil. A crucible with a hairline crack gives a dull ring.
   • A crucible that glows red has a temperature near 1100 °C. Below this temperature, a crucible may not glow red, but can cause a burn.
   • The ignition of magnesium ribbon is strongly exothermic and can crack a crucible. A few porcelain chips in the bottom of the crucible minimizes this problem, and can be weighed with the crucible and cover.
   • Heating copper and sulfur produces pungent sulfur dioxide gas. Avoid breathing the gas, and perform the reaction under a fume hood.
   • Dispose of chemical waste in the designated container.

Analysis of Alum

OBJECTIVES

- To determine the percentage of water in alum hydrate.
- To determine the percentage of water in an unknown hydrate.
- To calculate the water of crystallization for an unknown hydrate.
- To develop the laboratory skills for analyzing a hydrate.

DISCUSSION

A **hydrate** is a compound having a fixed number of water molecules. The number of water molecules is referred to as the **water of crystallization**, or water of hydration. For example, barium chloride dihydrate, $BaCl_2 \cdot 2H_2O$, has two waters of crystallization; and alum hydrate, $KAl(SO_4)_2 \cdot 12H_2O$, has twelve waters of crystallization. When heated, a hydrate loses water and produces an **anhydrous compound**. Alum is a hydrate compound used in styptic pencils to stop minor bleeding, and decomposes to an anhydrous compound as follows:

$$KAl(SO_4)_2 \cdot 12H_2O(s) \xrightarrow{\Delta} KAl(SO_4)_2(s) \ + \ 12\,H_2O(g)$$

alum	*anhydrous*	*water of*
hydrate	*compound*	*crystallization*

The theoretical percentage of water in a hydrate is found by comparing the mass of the water of crystallization to the mass of the hydrate. This is accomplished by dividing the total mass of water by the molar mass of the hydrate. Example Exercise 1 illustrates this calculation.

From Experiment 13 of *Laboratory Manual to Accompany Introductory Chemistry: Concepts and Critical Thinking*, Sixth Edition. Charles H. Corwin.

Example Exercise 1 • Theoretical % H$_2$O in Alum

Calculate the theoretical percentage of water in alum hydrate, $KAl(SO_4)_2 \cdot 12H_2O$.

Solution: The molar mass of $KAl(SO_4)_2 \cdot 12H_2O$ is found as follows:

K:	1	x	39.10 g	=	39.10 g
Al:	1	x	26.98 g	=	26.98 g
SO$_4$:	2	x	96.07 g	=	192.14 g
H$_2$O:	12	x	18.02 g	=	216.24 g
					474.46 g

The theoretical percentage of water is found by dividing the total mass of water (12 x 18.02 g) by the molar mass of the hydrate (474.46 g).

$$\frac{12 \times 18.02 \text{ g}}{474.46 \text{ g}} \quad \times \quad 100\% \quad = \quad 45.58\% \text{ H}_2\text{O}$$

Percentage of Water in Alum Hydrate

Experimentally, the amount of water is found from **weighing by difference**; that is, the difference in mass before and after heating the sample. For example, an alum hydrate sample is decomposed to give the following data:

mass of beaker and watchglass + alum hydrate	102.636 g
mass of beaker and watchglass	101.486 g
mass of beaker and watchglass + anhydrous compound	102.113 g

The mass of alum hydrate is: 102.636 g – 101.486 g = 1.150 g. The mass of water is the difference before and after heating the sample: 102.636 g – 102.113 g = 0.523 g. The calculation for the experimental percentage of water is illustrated in Example Exercise 2.

Example Exercise 2 • Experimental % H$_2$O in Alum

A 1.150-g sample of alum hydrate decomposes with heat and loses 0.523 g of water. Calculate the experimental percentage of water in alum sample.

Solution: The experimental percentage of water is simply

$$\frac{\text{mass of water}}{\text{mass of hydrate}} \quad \times \quad 100\% \quad = \quad \% \text{ water}$$

$$\frac{0.523 \text{ g}}{1.150 \text{ g}} \quad \times \quad 100\% \quad = \quad 45.5\% \text{ water}$$

In this experiment, we will heat a sample of alum hydrate to determine the percentage of water (Figure 1). After gaining experience analyzing the known alum sample, you will analyze an unknown hydrate.

Water of Crystallization in an Unknown Hydrate

After analyzing an alum sample, you will analyze an unknown hydrate for the percentage of water using the same procedure. You will also determine the water of crystallization for the unknown hydrate; that is, you will determine the value of X in an unknown hydrate, $AC \cdot X H_2O$.

Example Exercise 3 • Water of Crystallization for Unknown Hydrate

Calculate the water of crystallization for an unknown hydrate, $AC \cdot X H_2O$, that is found to contain 30.6% water. The molar mass of the anhydrous compound (AC) is 245 g/mol.

Solution: If the amount of water in the unknown hydrate is 30.6%, the anhydrous compound must be 69.4% (100% – 30.6% = 69.4%). If we assume a 100.0-g sample, the mass of water is 30.6 g and the anhydrous compound is 69.4 g. We can calculate the moles of water and anhydrous compound as follows.

$$30.6 \ \cancel{g \ H_2O} \quad \times \quad \frac{1 \ mol \ H_2O}{18.02 \ \cancel{g \ H_2O}} \quad = \quad 1.70 \ mol \ H_2O$$

$$69.4 \ \cancel{g \ AC} \quad \times \quad \frac{1 \ mol \ AC}{245 \ \cancel{g \ AC}} \quad = \quad 0.283 \ mol \ AC$$

To find the water of crystallization we simply divide the moles of water by the moles of anhydrous compound. Thus,

$$\frac{1.70 \ mol \ H_2O}{0.283 \ mol \ AC} \quad = \quad 6.01 \approx 6$$

Since the water of crystallization must be a whole number, we round off 6.01 to the nearest whole number (6). The formula for the hydrate is $AC \cdot 6H_2O$.

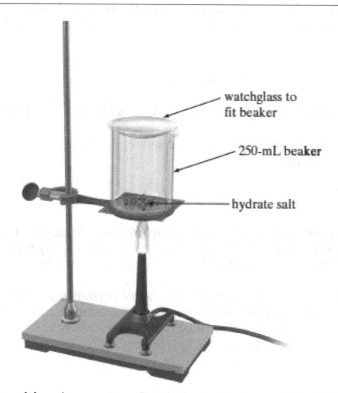

— watchglass to fit beaker

— 250-mL beaker

— hydrate salt

Figure 1 Decomposition Apparatus Gently heat a hydrate salt in the beaker to release steam and avoid spattering.

EQUIPMENT and CHEMICALS

- wire gauze
- 250-mL beaker
- watchglass
- ring stand & ring

- alum, $KAl(SO_4)_2 \cdot 12H_2O$
- unknown hydrate samples

PROCEDURE

A. Percentage of Water in Alum Hydrate

1. Weigh a clean, dry, 250-mL beaker covered with a watchglass. Add about 0.8–1.2 g of alum hydrate into the beaker, and reweigh.

2. Support the beaker and watchglass on a ring stand using a wire gauze (Figure 1). Gently heat the hydrate and observe moisture on the sides of the beaker and bottom of the watchglass. Continue heating until all the moisture is evaporated. When the hydrate is completely decomposed, it will change from crystalline to powder.

   Note: If the watchglass is not completely dry, hold it carefully with crucible tongs over a low burner flame until no moisture remains.

RECYCLE
Chemical
Waste

3. Turn off the burner, and allow the beaker to cool for 10 minutes. Carefully transfer the beaker with the watchglass to the balance. Weigh the mass of the beaker, watchglass, and anhydrous compound.

4. Discard the decomposed alum and clean the beaker. Perform a second trial with alum hydrate. Calculate the percentage of water in the hydrate for each trial and the average value.

B. Percentage of Water in an Unknown Hydrate

1. Obtain an unknown hydrate from the Instructor, and record the unknown number.

2. Repeat steps 1–4 as in Procedure A, and report the average percentage of water in the unknown hydrate.

C. Water of Crystallization in an Unknown Hydrate

1. Given the molar mass of the anhydrous compound from the Instructor, calculate the water of crystallization. The Instructor may wish to verify the experimental percentage of water before giving the molar mass of the unknown hydrate.

   Note: It is not unusual for the water of crystallization value to differ by a few tenths from a whole number; for example, 2.1 or 6.7. However, the water of crystallization must be rounded to a whole number. In this example, 2.1 is rounded to 2 and 6.7 is rounded to 7.

EXPERIMENT   NAME   _____

DATE   _____   SECTION   _____

PRELABORATORY ASSIGNMENT*

1. Provide the key term that corresponds to each of the following definitions.

    _____ (a) a substance that contains a specific number of water molecules attached to a formula unit in a crystalline compound

    _____ (b) the number of water molecules bound to a formula unit in a hydrate

    _____ (c) a compound that does not contain water

    _____ (d) a procedure for obtaining the mass of a sample indirectly by first weighing a container and then weighing the container with the sample

    _____ (e) a repeated process of heating, cooling, and weighing until the mass readings for an object are constant, or agree closely

    _____ (f) the mass of 1 mole of any substance expressed in grams

    _____ (g) the amount of substance that contains Avogadro's number of particles

    Key Terms: anhydrous compound, hydrate, heating to constant weight, molar mass (MM), mole (mol), water of crystallization, weighing by difference

2. If you weigh a bag of microwave popcorn, before and after heating, does the popped corn weigh more or less than the unpopped kernels?

3. How can you tell when to stop heating a hydrate because it is decomposed completely?

4. How will the weighing be affected by placing a warm beaker on the balance?

5. What are major sources of experimental error?

_____

* *Answers at the end of the experiment.*

6. An alum hydrate sample was analyzed by decomposition and gave the following data:

mass of beaker and watchglass + alum hydrate	102.218 g
mass of beaker and watchglass	101.286 g
mass of beaker and watchglass + anhydrous compound	101.798 g

Refer to Example Exercise 2 and show the calculation for the percentage of water.

Does the experimental result agree with the theoretical value shown in Example Exercise 1?

7. An unknown hydrate (AC • X H_2O) was found to contain 30.5% water. Assume the molar mass of the anhydrous compound (AC) is 164 g/mol. Refer to Example Exercise 3 and show the calculation for the water of crystallization and formula for the hydrate.

Water of crystallization _____   Formula of hydrate   AC • ____H_2O

8. What safety precautions must be observed in this experiment?

EXPERIMENT _____   NAME _____

DATE _____   SECTION _____

DATA TABLE

A. Percentage of Water in Alum Hydrate

mass of beaker and watchglass + alum hydrate
(before heating) _____ g   _____ g

mass of beaker and watchglass _____ g   _____ g

mass of alum hydrate _____ g   _____ g

mass of beaker and watchglass + anhydrous compound _____ g   _____ g
(after heating)

mass of water _____ g   _____ g
(before heating – after heating)

RECYCLE
Chemical
Waste

Show the calculation for the percentage of water for trial 1 (see Example Exercise 2).

Percentage of water in $KAl(SO_4)_2 \cdot 12H_2O$ _____ %   _____ %

Average percentage of water   _____ %

189

B. Percentage of Water in an Unknown Hydrate   **UNKNOWN #** _____

mass of beaker and watchglass + unknown hydrate   _____ g   _____ g
(before heating)

mass of beaker and watchglass   _____ g   _____ g

mass of unknown hydrate   _____ g   _____ g

mass of beaker and watchglass + anhydrous compound   _____ g   _____ g
(after heating)

mass of water   _____ g   _____ g
(before heating – after heating)

Show the calculation for the percentage of water for trial 1 (see Example Exercise 2).

Percentage of water in the unknown hydrate   _____ %   _____ %

Average percentage of water   _____ %

C. Water of Crystallization in an Unknown Hydrate

molar mass of anhydrous compound (AC)   _____ g/mol
(see Instructor)

percentage of water (see Procedure B)   _____ %

percentage of anhydrous compound (AC)   _____ %

Show the calculation for the water of crystallization (see Example Exercise 3).

Water of crystallization   _____   Formula of hydrate   AC•____H_2O

EXPERIMENT   NAME _____   191

DATE _____   SECTION _____

POSTLABORATORY ASSIGNMENT

1. Calculate the theoretical percentage of water for the following hydrates.

    (a) sodium carbonate hexahydrate, $Na_2CO_3 \cdot 6H_2O$

    _____

    (b) sodium carbonate decahydrate, $Na_2CO_3 \cdot 10H_2O$

    _____

2. An unknown hydrate, $AC \cdot XH_2O$, has a mass of 1.000 g before heating, and a mass of 0.738 g after heating. What is the experimental percentage of water in the hydrate?

    _____

3. If the anhydrous compound (AC) in the preceding problem has a molar mass of 101 g/mol, what is the water of crystallization (X) and the formula for the hydrate?

    Water of crystallization _____   Formula of hydrate $AC \cdot$____H_2O

4. A hydrate of nickel(II) chloride, $NiCl_2 \cdot XH_2O$, decomposes to produce 21.8% water. Calculate the water of crystallization (X), and write the formula for the hydrate.

        Water of crystallization   _____   Formula of hydrate $NiCl_2 \cdot$____H_2O

5. A different hydrate of nickel(II) chloride, $NiCl_2 \cdot XH_2O$, decomposes to produce 45.5% water. Calculate the water of crystallization (X), and write the formula for the hydrate.

        Water of crystallization   _____   Formula of hydrate $NiCl_2 \cdot$____H_2O

6. (optional) A blue turquoise is an example of a hydrate mineral containing copper; the chemical formula is $CuAl_6(PO_4)_4(OH)_8 \cdot 4H_2O$. What is the percent water in this semiprecious stone?

_____

ANSWERS TO PRELABORATORY ASSIGNMENTS

1. See the Glossary.
2. The popped corn *weighs less* than the unpopped kernels because steam escapes. Similarly, the mass of the anhydrous compound *weighs less* than the hydrate because steam escapes.
3. The hydrate is completely decomposed when moisture inside the beaker is gone. The sample will change in appearance from crystals (*before heating*) to powder (*after heating*).
4. A warm beaker radiates heat and warms the air around the balance pan. This warm air rises and lifts the balance pan causing a light mass reading.
5. • Not allowing the beaker to cool causes a light weighing, which gives *high results*.
   • Moisture on the watchglass causes a heavy weighing, which gives *low results*.
   • Incomplete heating of the hydrate causes a heavy weighing, which gives *low results*.
   • Overheating the hydrate can decompose the anhydrous compound, which gives *high results*.
6. $(0.420 \text{ g} / 0.932 \text{ g}) \times 100\% = 45.2\%$
   The experimental result of 45.2% agrees with the theoretical value of 45.58%.
7. $(30.5 \text{ g} / 18.02 \text{ g/mol} = 1.69 \text{ mol } H_2O)$; $(69.5 \text{ g} / 164 \text{ g/mol} = 0.424 \text{ mol AC})$
   After dividing mol H_2O by mol AC (1.69 mol / 0.424 mol), the water of crystallization is found to be 4, and the formula is $AC \cdot 4H_2O$.
8. • Wear safety goggles; be careful when using the laboratory burner.
   • Heat the watchglass gently above a *low* burner flame to avoid breakage.
   • When weighing the beaker and watchglass, handle carefully to avoid breakage.
   • Dispose of chemical waste in the designated container.

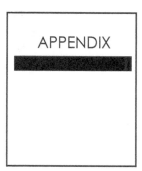
Laboratory Burner

Although a variety of lab burners are found in chemistry laboratories, they all employ the same principle. Natural gas is allowed to flow into the barrel of the burner and mix with the air. The ratio of gas to air can be adjusted, which in turn regulates the temperature of the flame. The more air that is available, the hotter the flame. The hottest part of the flame is the tip of the inner pale blue cone. Two typical burners are shown in Figure 1.

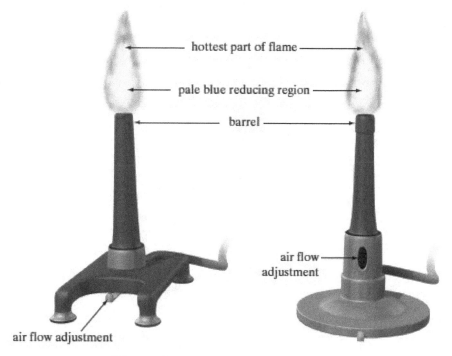

Figure 1 Laboratory Burners

Steps in Operating a Burner

1. Close the air flow adjustment.
2. Open the gas jet.
3. Light the burner at the top of the barrel.
4. To obtain a hotter flame, open the air flow adjustment.
5. To shut off the burner, close the gas jet.

From Appendix A of *Laboratory Manual to Accompany Introductory Chemistry: Concepts and Critical Thinking*, Sixth Edition.
Charles H. Corwin. Copyright © 2013 by Pearson Education, Inc. All rights reserved.

Milligram Balance

An electronic milligram balance provides measurements with an uncertainty of one milligram (± 0.001 g). The mass is determined by placing a sample on the pan, closing the draft shield doors, and reading the digital display. Tenth milligram electronic balances are also common, which have an uncertainty of one-tenth milligram (± 0.0001 g).

Figure 1   A digital electronic balance with milligram precision (± 0.001 g).
(Photo courtesy of Mettler Toledo Corporation)

From Appendix D of *Laboratory Manual to Accompany Introductory Chemistry: Concepts and Critical Thinking*, Sixth Edition. Charles H. Corwin. Copyright © 2013 by Pearson Education, Inc. All rights reserved.

Activity Series for Metals

MOST ACTIVE METAL: $Li \rightarrow Li^+ + e^-$

$K \rightarrow K^+ + e^-$

$Ba \rightarrow Ba^{2+} + 2e^-$

$Sr \rightarrow Sr^{2+} + 2e^-$

$Ca \rightarrow Ca^{2+} + 2e^-$

$Na \rightarrow Na^+ + e^-$

(metals above Mg react with water at 25 °C)

$Mg \rightarrow Mg^{2+} + 2e^-$

$Al \rightarrow Al^{3+} + 3e^-$

$Mn \rightarrow Mn^{2+} + 2e^-$

$Zn \rightarrow Zn^{2+} + 2e^-$

$Cr \rightarrow Cr^{3+} + 3e^-$

$Fe \rightarrow Fe^{2+} + 2e^-$

$Cd \rightarrow Cd^{2+} + 2e^-$

$Co \rightarrow Co^{2+} + 2e^-$

$Ni \rightarrow Ni^{2+} + 2e^-$

$Sn \rightarrow Sn^{2+} + 2e^-$

$Pb \rightarrow Pb^{2+} + 2e^-$

(metals above H^+ react with acid)

$\mathbf{H_2 \rightarrow 2\,H^+ + 2\,e^-}$

(metals below H_2 do not react with acid)

$Cu \rightarrow Cu^{2+} + 2e^-$

$Ag \rightarrow Ag^+ + e^-$

$Hg \rightarrow Hg^{2+} + 2e^-$

LEAST ACTIVE METAL: $Au \rightarrow Au^{3+} + 3e^-$

APPENDIX

Solubility Rules

Ionic compounds containing the following ions are generally soluble in water:

1. alkali metal ions and ammonium ions, Li^+, Na^+, K^+, NH_4^+

2. acetate ion, $C_2H_3O_2^-$

3. nitrate ion, NO_3^-

4. halide ions ($X = Cl^-$, Br^-, I^-)
   (AgX, Hg_2X_2, and PbX_2 are exceptions and *insoluble*)

5. sulfate ion, SO_4^{2-}
   ($SrSO_4$, $BaSO_4$, and $PbSO_4$ are exceptions and *insoluble*)

Ionic compounds containing the following ions are generally insoluble* in water:

6. carbonate ion, CO_3^{2-}
   (see Rule 1 exceptions, which are *soluble*)

7. chromate ion, CrO_4^{2-}
   (see Rule 1 exceptions, which are *soluble*)

8. phosphate ion, PO_4^{3-}
   (see Rule 1 exceptions, which are *soluble*)

9. sulfide ion, S^{2-}
   (CaS, SrS, BaS, and Rule 1 exceptions are *soluble*)

10. hydroxide ion, OH^-
    [$Ca(OH)_2$, $Sr(OH)_2$, $Ba(OH)_2$, and Rule 1 are exceptions and *soluble*]

---

* These ionic compounds are actually slightly soluble, or very slightly soluble, in water.

From Appendix G of *Laboratory Manual to Accompany Introductory Chemistry: Concepts and Critical Thinking*, Sixth Edition. Charles H. Corwin. Copyright © 2013 by Pearson Education, Inc. All rights reserved.

Common Monoatomic Anions

Anion	Name	Anion	Name
Br^-	bromide ion	N^{3-}	nitride ion
Cl^-	chloride ion	O^{2-}	oxide ion
F^-	fluoride ion	P^{3-}	phosphide ion
I^-	iodide ion	S^{2-}	sulfide ion

Common Polyatomic Cations

Cation	Name	Cation	Name
NH_4^+	ammonium ion	H_3O^+	hydronium ion

Common Polyatomic Anions

Anion	Name	Anion	Name
$C_2H_3O_2^-$	acetate ion	OH^-	hydroxide ion
CO_3^{2-}	carbonate ion	ClO^-	hypochlorite ion
ClO_3^-	chlorate ion	NO_3^-	nitrate ion
ClO_2^-	chlorite ion	NO_2^-	nitrite ion
CrO_4^{2-}	chromate ion	ClO_4^-	perchlorate ion
CN^-	cyanide ion	MnO_4^-	permanganate ion
$Cr_2O_7^{2-}$	dichromate ion	PO_4^{3-}	phosphate ion
HCO_3^-	hydrogen carbonate ion	SO_4^{2-}	sulfate ion
HSO_4^-	hydrogen sulfate ion	SO_3^{2-}	sulfite ion

Common Monoatomic Cations

—Stock System

Cation	Name	Cation	Name
Al^{3+}	aluminum ion	Li^+	lithium ion
Ba^{2+}	barium ion	Mg^{2+}	magnesium ion
Cd^{2+}	cadmium ion	Mn^{2+}	manganese(II) ion
Ca^{2+}	calcium ion	Hg_2^{2+}	mercury(I) ion
Co^{2+}	cobalt(II) ion	Hg^{2+}	mercury(II) ion
Co^{3+}	cobalt(III) ion	Ni^{2+}	nickel(II) ion
Cu^+	copper(I) ion	K^+	potassium ion
Cu^{2+}	copper(II) ion	Ag^+	silver ion
Cr^{3+}	chromium(III) ion	Na^+	sodium ion
H^+	hydrogen ion	Sr^{2+}	strontium ion
Fe^{2+}	iron(II) ion	Sn^{2+}	tin(II) ion
Pb^{2+}	lead(II) ion	Sn^{4+}	tin(IV) ion
Pb^{4+}	lead(IV) ion	Zn^{2+}	zinc ion

—Latin System

Cation	Name	Cation	Name
Co^{2+}	cobaltous ion	Pb^{2+}	plumbous ion
Co^{3+}	cobaltic ion	Pb^{4+}	plumbic ion
Cu^+	cuprous ion	Hg_2^{2+}	mercurous ion
Cu^{2+}	cupric ion	Hg^{2+}	mercuric ion
Fe^{2+}	ferrous ion	Sn^{2+}	stannous ion
Fe^{3+}	ferric ion	Sn^{4+}	stannic ion

Glossary

APPENDIX

Glossary

–A–

abscissa The horizontal axis (x-axis) on a graph.

activity series A relative order of metals arranged in a list according to their ability to undergo reaction. A metal higher in the series will displace another metal from its aqueous solution.

actual yield The amount of product experimentally obtained from a reaction.

alkali metal Any Group IA/1 element in the periodic table, excluding hydrogen.

alkaline earth metal Any Group IIA/2 element in the periodic table.

anhydrous compound A compound that does not contain water.

anion Any negatively charged ion.

aqueous solution A solution of a substance dissolved in water.

atmospheric pressure The pressure exerted by the air molecules in Earth's atmosphere; atmospheric pressure is measured with a barometer.

"atomic fingerprint" The unique line spectrum that is characteristic of a given element and can be used for identification.

Avogadro's number (N) The value that corresponds to the number of carbon atoms in 12.01 g of carbon; 6.02×10^{23} particles.

–B–

Balmer formula A mathematical formula for calculating the wavelength of light emitted from an excited hydrogen atom when the electron drops to the second energy level.

biochemistry The study of compounds derived from plants and animals.

–C–

carbonyl group The C=O group, which is present in aldehydes, ketones, carboxylic acids, esters, and amides.

catalyst A substance that speeds up a chemical reaction.

cation Any positively charged ion.

centimeter (cm) A metric unit of length; 100 cm = 1 m.

centrifuge An instrument that spins test tubes in order to separate a precipitate from solution. The act of rapidly spinning a test tube in order to separate a precipitate from solution.

change of state The conversion from one physical state to another; for example, the change in a substance from a liquid to a solid.

chemical change A modification of a substance that alters its chemical composition.

chemical property A characteristic of a substance that cannot be observed without changing its chemical formula.

chemistry The branch of science that studies the composition and properties of matter.

chromatography A method for separating a mixture into its components as a result of a varying attraction of compounds for a mobile solvent on a stationary solid.

class of compounds A family of compounds in which all the members have the same structural feature (that is, an atom or group of atoms) and similar chemical properties.

combined gas law The pressure exerted by a gas is inversely proportional to its volume and directly proportional to its Kelvin temperature.

compound A pure substance that can be broken down into two or more simpler substances by chemical reaction.

condition The act of rinsing glassware (e.g., a graduated cylinder, pipet, or buret) with a sample liquid to avoid dilution by water on the inside surface.

continuous spectrum A broad uninterrupted band of radiant energy.

coprecipitation A term that refers to a precipitate containing impurities that are usually soluble.

covalent bond A bond characterized by the sharing of one or more pairs of valence electrons.

–D–

Dalton's law of partial pressures The pressure exerted by a mixture of gases is equal to the sum of the pressures exerted by each gas in the mixture.

decant The process of pouring a liquid from one container into another; for example, pouring the supernate from one test tube into a second test tube.

density (*d*) The amount of mass in a unit volume of matter; for example, g/mL.

digestion The process of heating a precipitate in aqueous solution to develop larger particles that are easier to filter and free of impurities.

dissociation The process of an ionic compound dissolving in water and separating into positive and negative ions.

double bond A bond composed of two electron pairs shared between two atoms. A double bond is represented by two dashes between the symbols of the two atoms.

–E–

electron dot formula A diagram of a molecule in which each atom is represented by its chemical symbol surrounded by two dots for each pair of bonding or nonbonding electrons.

element A pure substance that cannot be broken down any further by ordinary chemical reaction.

empirical formula The chemical formula of a compound that expresses the simplest whole number ratio of atoms of each element in a molecule, or ions in a formula unit.

endpoint The stage in a titration when the indicator changes color.

experiment A scientific procedure for collecting data and recording observations under controlled conditions.

experimental conditions The conditions of temperature and pressure at which a gas sample is collected; not usually STP.

–F–

filtrate The solution that passes through filter paper in a filtration operation.

firing to red heat Heating a crucible or other porcelain object until it glows red.

flame test A means of identifying a substance by observing the characteristic color it emits when placed in a hot flame.

freezing point The temperature at which a liquid substance crystallizes and forms a solid.

frequency The number of times a light wave travels a complete cycle in one second.

functional group An atom or group of atoms that characterizes a class of compounds, and contributes to their similar physical and chemical properties.

–G–

gram (g) A metric unit of mass; 1000 g = 1 kg.

group A vertical column in the periodic table; a family of elements having similar properties.

–H–

halide A negatively charged Group VIIA/17 element; for example, bromide, chloride, or iodide.

halogen A Group VIIA/17 element; for example, chlorine, bromine, or iodine.

heating to constant weight A repeated process of heating, cooling, and weighing until the mass readings for an object are constant, or agree closely.

heterogeneous mixture Matter having an indefinite composition and properties that can vary within the sample.

homogeneous mixture Matter having a definite composition but properties that can vary from sample to sample; examples include alloys, solutions, and gas mixtures.

hydrate A substance that contains a specific number of water molecules attached to a formula unit in a crystalline compound.

hydrocarbon A compound containing only hydrogen and carbon.

hydrocarbon derivative A compound containing carbon, hydrogen, and another element such as oxygen, nitrogen, or a halogen.

hypothesis A tentative proposal of a scientific principle that attempts to explain the meaning of a set of data collected in an experiment.

–I–

immiscible A term that refers to liquids that do not dissolve in one another and separate into two layers.

indicator A chemical substance that undergoes a color change according to the pH of a solution; for example, phenolphthalein is colorless below pH 9 and pink above pH 9.

ionization The process of a polar molecular compound dissolving in water and forming positive and negative ions.

isomers Compounds with the same molecular formula but with different structural formulas. Isomers have different physical and chemical properties.

–L–

light A specific term that refers to the portion of the radiant energy spectrum that is visible; that is, violet through red. A general term that refers to all forms of radiant energy.

like dissolves like **rule** The general principle that solubility is greatest when the polarity of the solute and solvent are similar.

line spectrum The narrow bands of light observed through a spectroscope that are emitted from excited atoms in a gas discharge tube.

–M–

mass The amount of matter in a sample. Mass is independent of Earth's gravitational attraction and is the quantity measured with a laboratory balance.

mass/mass percent concentration (m/m %) A solution concentration expression that relates the mass of solute in grams dissolved in each 100 grams of solution.

$$\frac{\text{mass of solute}}{\text{mass of solution}} \times 100\% = \text{m/m \%}$$

melting point The temperature at which a solid substance melts and forms a liquid.

meniscus A clear lens at the surface of a liquid inside a piece of narrow glassware, such as a graduated cylinder, pipet, or buret.

metric system A decimal system of measurement using prefixes and a basic unit to express physical quantities such as length, mass, and volume.

milliliter (mL) A metric unit of volume; 1000 mL = 1 L.

miscible A term that refers to liquids that dissolve completely in one another.

mobile phase A term that refers to the solvent that travels up a paper chromatogram by capillary action.

molar concentration (*M*) A solution concentration expression that relates the moles of solute dissolved in each liter of solution; also referred to as molarity.

$$\frac{\text{moles of solute}}{\text{liters of solution}} = M$$

molar mass (MM) The mass of 1 mole of any substance expressed in grams. (The individual particles that compose the substance may be atoms, molecules, or formula units.)

molar volume The volume occupied by 1 mole of any gas at STP; at 0°C and 760 mm Hg, the volume of 1 mole of any gas is 22.4 L (22,400 mL).

mole (mol) The amount of substance that contains Avogadro's number of particles; that is, an amount of substance that contains 6.02×10^{23} particles.

molecular formula The chemical formula of a compound that expresses the actual number of atoms of each element in a molecule.

monolayer A thin film layer of organic molecules on the surface of water; the monolayer is only 1 molecule thick.

–N–

nanometer (nm) A unit of length used to express wavelengths of light; a unit of length equal to one-billionth of a meter.

net ionic equation A chemical equation that portrays an ionic reaction after spectator ions have been canceled from the total ionic equation. The net ionic equation shows only those species undergoing a change during a chemical reaction.

nonpolar "tail" The portion of a long organic molecule having nonpolar bonds.

–O–

octet rule The statement that an atom tends to bond in such a way so as to acquire eight electrons in its outer shell. A hydrogen atom is an exception to the rule and acquires only two valence electrons.

ordinate The vertical axis (y-axis) on a graph.

organic chemistry The study of carbon-containing compounds.

origin The point of intersection of the horizontal and vertical axes on a graph.

oxidation A chemical process characterized by the loss of electrons. A process in which a substance undergoes an increase in oxidation number.

oxidation number A positive or negative value assigned to an atom in a substance according to a set of rules. A value that indicates whether an atom is electron poor or electron rich compared to the free atom. Metals and nonmetals in the free state have an oxidation number of zero.

oxidizing agent A substance that causes the oxidation of another substance in a redox reaction. The substance that is reduced in a redox reaction.

–P–

percent yield The actual yield compared to the theoretical yield expressed as a percent.

period A horizontal row in the periodic table; a series of elements with properties that vary from metallic to nonmetallic.

periodic law The properties of the elements recur in a repeating pattern when arranged according to increasing atomic number.

photon A particle of light that corresponds to a unit of radiant energy. A photon may also be referred to as a quantum (*pl.*, quanta).

physical change A modification of a substance that does not alter its chemical composition; for example, a change in physical state.

physical property A characteristic of a substance that can be observed without changing its chemical formula.

physical state The condition of a substance existing as a solid, liquid, or gas.

polar "head" The portion of a long organic molecule having polar bonds.

precipitate (ppt) An insoluble solid substance produced from a reaction in aqueous solution.

product A substance resulting from a chemical reaction.

–Q–

qualitative analysis A systematic procedure for the separation and identification of cations, anions, or other substances present in a sample.

–R–

reactant A substance undergoing a chemical reaction.

redox reaction A chemical reaction that involves electron transfer and causes reduction of one species and oxidation of another.

reducing agent A substance that causes the reduction of another substance in a redox reaction. The substance that is oxidized in a redox reaction.

reduction A chemical process characterized by the gain of electrons. A process in which a substance undergoes a decrease in oxidation number.

R$_f$ value The ratio of the distance traveled by a sample component compared to the distance traveled by the solvent.

Rydberg equation A general mathematical equation for calculating the wavelength of light emitted from an excited hydrogen atom when the electron drops to any lower energy level.

–S–

saturated hydrocarbon A hydrocarbon containing only single bonds.

science The methodical exploration of nature and the logical explanation of the observations.

scientific method A systematic investigation that involves performing an experiment, proposing a hypothesis, testing the hypothesis, and stating a theory or law that explains a scientific principle.

single bond A bond composed of one electron pair shared between two atoms. A single bond is represented by a dash between the symbols of the two atoms.

solute The component of a solution that is the lesser quantity.

solvent The component of a solution that is the greater quantity.

solvent front The leading edge of the solvent, which travels from the bottom of the developing chamber to the upper portion of the chromatogram.

spectator ions Those ions in aqueous solution that do not participate in a reaction, and do not appear in the net ionic equation.

standard conditions See standard temperature and pressure.

standard solution A solution whose concentration has been established precisely (usually by titration to 3 or 4 significant digits).

standard temperature and pressure (STP) A temperature of 0°C and a pressure of 1 atm. A temperature of 273 K and a pressure of 760 mm Hg for a gas.

stationary phase A term that refers to the moisture that is strongly adsorbed onto a paper chromatogram and is not free to travel.

stoichiometry The relationship of quantities (i.e., mass of substance or volume of gas) in a chemical reaction according to the balanced chemical equation.

strong electrolyte An aqueous solution that is a good conductor of electricity and produces a bright glow from a light bulb in a conductivity apparatus.

structural formula A diagram of a molecule or polyatomic ion that shows the chemical symbol of each atom and a dash representing each pair of bonding electrons.

sublimation The direct change of state from a solid to a gas without forming a liquid. Conversely, the direct change of state from a gas to a solid is called deposition.

substance Matter having constant composition with definite and predictable properties.

supernate The solution above a precipitate after insoluble particles are separated from solution.

supersaturated solution A solution containing more solute than can ordinarily dissolve at a given temperature. A supersaturated solution is unstable and the excess solute will crystallize from solution if a seed crystal is added.

surface area Specifically, the region occupied by a single layer of organic molecules floating on water; the formula for calculating the surface area of a circle is $\pi d^2/4$.

–T–

tare weighing A procedure for obtaining the mass of a sample *directly* by placing a container on an electronic balance and setting the balance to zero. Second, add a sample to the container and record the mass of sample directly.

theoretical yield The amount of product that is calculated from a given amount of reactant.

theory An extensively tested proposal of a scientific principle that explains the behavior of nature. A theory offers a model, for example the atomic theory, to describe nature.

titration A laboratory procedure for delivering a measured volume of solution using a buret.

total ionic equation A chemical equation that portrays highly ionized substances in the ionic form and slightly ionized substances in the nonionized form.

triple bond A bond composed of three electron pairs shared between two atoms. A triple bond is represented by three dashes between the symbols of the two atoms.

–U–

uncertainty A term that refers to the degree of inexactness in an instrumental measurement; for example, ± 0.05 cm, ± 0.001 g, ± 0.5 mL, $\pm 0.5°C$, or ± 1 s.

unsaturated hydrocarbon A hydrocarbon containing a carbon-carbon double or triple bond.

–V–

valence electrons The electrons in the outermost s and p sublevels of an atom that form chemical bonds.

vapor pressure The pressure exerted by gaseous vapor above a liquid in a closed container when the rates of evaporation and condensation are equal; for example, the pressure exerted by water vapor above liquid water.

visible spectrum Light energy that is observed as violet, blue, green, yellow, orange, and red; the region in the radiant energy spectrum from approximately 400–700 nm.

volume by displacement A technique for determining the volume of a sample by measuring the volume of water it displaces.

–W–

water of crystallization The number of water molecules bound to a formula unit in a hydrate; also called *water of hydration*.

wavelength (λ) The distance a light wave travels to complete one cycle.

weak electrolyte An aqueous solution that is a poor conductor of electricity and produces a dim glow from a light bulb in a conductivity apparatus.

weighing by difference A procedure for obtaining the mass of a sample *indirectly* by first weighing a container and then weighing the container with the sample.

Index

Unsaturated hydrocarbon, 212